GEORGIA MATHEMATICS 1

Second Edition

Student Text

Carnegie Learning®

THE COGNITIVE TUTOR® COMPANY

Carnegie Learning®
THE COGNITIVE TUTOR® COMPANY

Pittsburgh, PA
Phone 888.851.7094
Fax 412.690.2444

www.carnegielearning.com

Acknowledgements

We would like to thank those listed below who helped to prepare the Cognitive Tutor®
Georgia Mathematics 1 Student Text.

William S. Hadley
Jaclyn Snyder
Jan Sinopoli
The Carnegie Learning Development Team

Mathematics was used in a variety of ways to create the building on the front cover. Architects designed the front of the building with curves that were structurally sound and pleasing to the eye. Interior designers created windows and rooms which optimized the use of ambient light while minimizing heating and cooling costs. As you work through the Cognitive Tutor® *Georgia Mathematics 1* text and software, you will see additional opportunities for using mathematics in your everyday activities.

ISBN 978-1-934800-26-3
Student Text

Printed in the United States of America
1-4/2008 HPS
2-4/2009 HPS

Dear Student,

You are about to begin an exciting adventure using mathematics, the language of science and technology. As you sit in front of a computer screen or video game, ride in an automobile, fly in a plane, talk on a cellular phone, or use any of the tools of modern society, realize that mathematics was critical in its invention, design, and production.

The workplace today demands that employees be technologically literate, work well in teams, and be self-starters. At Carnegie Learning, we have designed a mathematics course that uses state-of-the-art computer software with collaborative classroom activities.

As you use the Cognitive Tutor® *Georgia Mathematics 1* software, it actually learns about you as you learn about mathematics. As you work, you will receive "just-in-time" instruction so that you are always ready for the next problem. In the classroom, you will work with your peers to solve real-world problem situations. Working in groups, you will learn to use multiple representations to analyze questions and write or present your answers.

Throughout the entire process, your teacher will be a facilitator and guide in support of your learning. As a result, you will become a self-sufficient learner, moving through the software and Student Text at your own rate and discovering solutions to problems that you never thought were possible to solve.

Throughout this year, have fun while Learning by Doing!

The Cognitive Tutor® *Georgia Mathematics 1* Development Team

Contents

6 Properties of Quadrilaterals ● p. 255

7 Counting Methods and Probability ● p. 291

8 Data Analysis ● p. 339

Contents

Contents

Contents

Relations and Functions

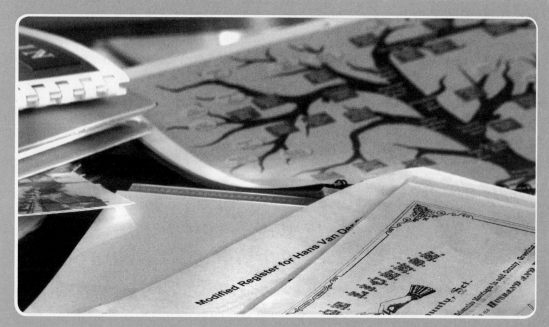

Genealogy is the study of family histories. Genealogists investigate birth, marriage, and death records to learn about families' past generations. You will use exponential functions to calculate how many direct ancestors you had a certain number of generations ago.

Mathematical Representations

INTRODUCTION   Mathematics is a human invention, developed as people encountered problems that they could not solve. For instance, when people first began to accumulate possessions, they needed to answer questions such as: How many? How many more? How many less?

People responded by developing the concepts of numbers and counting. Mathematics made a huge leap when people began using symbols to represent numbers. The first "numerals" were probably tally marks used to count weapons, livestock, or food.

As society grew more complex, people needed to answer questions such as: Who has more? How much does each person get? If there are 5 members in my family, 6 in your family, and 10 in another family, how can each person receive the same amount?

During this course, we will solve problems and work with many different representations of mathematical concepts, ideas, and processes to better understand our world. The following processes can help you solve problems.

Discuss to Understand

- Read the problem carefully.
- What is the context of the problem? Do you understand it?
- What is the question that you are being asked? Does it make sense?

Think for Yourself

- Do I need any additional information to answer the question?
- Is this problem similar to some other problem that I know?
- How can I represent the problem using a picture, a diagram, symbols, or some other representation?

Work with Your Partner

- How did you do the problem?
- Show me your representation.
- This is the way I thought about the problem—how did you think about it?
- What else do we need to solve the problem?
- Does our reasoning and our answer make sense to one another?

Work with Your Group

- Show me your representation.
- This is the way I thought about the problem—how did you think about it?
- What else do we need to solve the problem?
- Does our reasoning and our answer make sense to one another?
- How can we explain our solution to one another? To the class?

Share with the Class

- Here is our solution and how we solved it.
- We could only get this far with our solution. How can we finish?
- Could we have used a different strategy to solve the problem?

1.1 Human Growth
Multiple Representations of Relations and Functions

Objectives

In this lesson you will:

- Represent relations and functions using tables, graphs, words, and algebraic equations.
- Determine the domain and range of a relation.
- Determine if relations are functions.
- Describe the graphs of relations and functions.
- Use graphs to make predictions.

Key Terms

- relation
- domain
- range
- function

Problem 1   Age and Height

The following table shows values for the relation between age from 6 months to 13 years and the average height of boys.

Take Note

A **relation** is a mapping between a set of inputs and a set of outputs.

Age	Average Height (inches)
6 months	26
12 months	30
18 months	34
2 years	36
3 years	39
4 years	42
5 years	44
6 years	47
7 years	49
8 years	51
9 years	53
10 years	55
11 years	57
12 years	59
13 years	61

1. Create a scatter plot of the relation between age and average height on the grid shown.

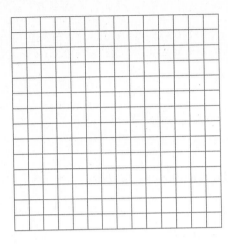

2. Does it make sense to connect the points of the scatter plot? Why or why not?

3. Describe the shape of the graph.

4. What is the increase in average height for boys

   a. between 6 months and 18 months?

   b. between 1 year and 2 years?

   c. between 2 years and 3 years?

   d. between 7 years and 8 years?

5. During what one-year period does the average height for boys increase the most?

   a. How would you use the table to answer this question?

   b. How would you use the graph to answer this question?

6. The set of inputs of a relation is the **domain.** What is the domain of the relation?

7. The set of outputs of a relation is the **range.** What is the range of the relation?

Take Note

A **function** is a relation that maps each member of the domain onto one and only one member of the range.

8. Is the relation a function? Explain.

9. Use the graph to answer each question.

   a. What is the average height of a 6½-year-old boy?

   b. What is the average height of a 14-year-old boy?

   c. At what age do boys have an average height of 54 inches?

10. The relation only includes ages up to 13 years.

    a. Using the graph, what would you predict as the increase in average height of boys from the ages of 13 years to 21 years?

    b. Using this predicted increase, what would be the average height at 21 years?

    c. Does this prediction make sense? Why or why not?

Problem 2 Age and Weight

The following table shows values for the relation between age from 6 months to 13 years and average weight for boys.

Age	Average Weight (pounds)
6 months	16
12 months	23
18 months	24
2 years	31
3 years	35
4 years	40
5 years	45
6 years	49
7 years	55
8 years	61
9 years	69
10 years	75
11 years	85
12 years	89
13 years	99

1. Create a scatter plot of the relation between age and average weight on the grid shown.

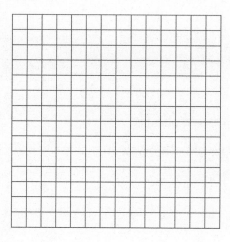

2. Does it make sense to connect the points of the scatter plot? Why or why not?

3. Describe the shape of the graph.

4. During what one-year period does the average weight of boys increase the most?

   a. How would you use the table to answer this question?

   b. How would you use the graph to answer this question?

5. What are the domain and range of the relation?

6. Is the relation a function? Explain.

7. Use the graph to answer each question.

   a. What is the average weight of a 6-year, 6-month-old boy?

   b. What is the average weight of a 14-year-old boy?

   c. At what age does a boy have an average weight of 65 pounds?

8. The relation only includes ages up to 13 years.

   a. Using the graph, what would you predict as the increase in average weight for boys from the ages of 13 years to 21 years?

   b. Using this predicted average increase, what would be the average weight for boys at 21 years?

   c. Does this prediction make sense? Why or why not?

Problem 3   Weight and Height

Dino's parents recorded his weight and height as he was growing up as shown in the table.

Dino's Age	Dino's Weight	Dino's Height
Years	Pounds	Inches
1	24	21
3	33	35
5	48	44
7	57	56
9	73	75
11	73	78
13	99	95

1. Create a scatter plot of the relation between Dino's weight and his height on the grid shown.

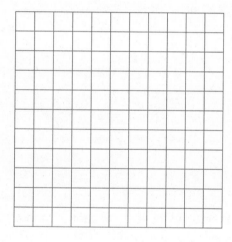

2. Does it make sense to connect the points of the scatter plot? Why or why not?

© 2009 Carnegie Learning, Inc.

3. What are the domain and range of the relation?

4. Is the relation a function? Explain.

Problem 4   U.S. Shirts

You have been hired at a custom T-shirt shop, U.S. Shirts. One of your jobs is to calculate the total cost of customers' orders. The shop charges $8 per shirt plus a one-time charge of $15 to set up the T-shirt design.

1. What is a one-time charge?

2. What is the total cost for an order of

    a. 3 shirts?

    b. 10 shirts?

    c. 100 shirts?

3. How many shirts can be ordered for each amount of money? What is the actual cost for an order with that number of shirts?

    a. $50

    b. $60

c. $220

4. Explain how to calculate the number of shirts that can be ordered for a given amount of money.

5. Enter the values you determined in Questions 2 and 3 in the following table.

Labels	Number of Shirts Ordered	Total Cost
Units	Shirts	Dollars

6. Create a scatter plot of the relation between the number of T-shirts ordered and the total cost.

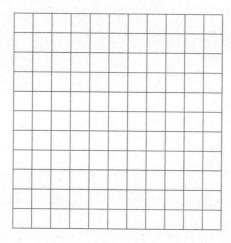

7. Does it make sense to connect the points of the scatter plot? Why or why not?

8. What are the domain and range of the relation?

9. Is the relation a function? Explain.

10. What are the variable quantities in this problem? Define a variable to represent each quantity.

11. Which variable quantity depends on the other variable quantity?

Take Note

A relation involves two quantities. One quantity, the dependent quantity, depends on the other, the independent quantity.

12. What is the independent quantity? What is the dependent quantity?

13. What are the constant quantities in this problem?

14. Use the variables from Question 10 to write an algebraic equation.

15. In this lesson, you represented problem situations using words, tables, graphs, and equations. What are the advantages and disadvantages of each representation?

	Advantages	Disadvantages
Words		
Tables		
Graphs		
Equations		

Be prepared to share your answers with the class.

1.2 Down and Up
Linear and Absolute Value Functions

Objectives

In this lesson you will:

- Model problem situations with linear and absolute value functions.
- Represent linear and absolute value functions using words, tables, equations, and graphs.
- Interpret the graphs of linear and absolute value functions.

Key Terms

- linear function
- slope
- extreme points/extrema
- absolute value function
- line symmetry
- line of symmetry

Problem 1 Water Tanks

Water is supplied to a house in the mountains using a well and a water tank. When full, the water tank contains 240 gallons of water. The occupants of the house use water at the average rate of 10 gallons per hour.

1. If the water tank begins full, how much water remains in the tank after

   a. 5 hours?

   b. 8 hours 30 minutes?

   c. 10 hours 15 minutes?

2. If the water tank begins full, after how long will the tank

   a. contain 100 gallons of water?

   b. contain 75 gallons of water?

   c. be one fourth full?

   d. be completely empty?

3. What are the variable quantities in this problem?

4. What is the independent quantity? What is the dependent quantity?

5. Use the values from Questions 1 and 2 to complete the following table.

	Independent Quantity	Dependent Quantity
Labels		
Units		

6. Create a scatter plot of the relation between the time and the amount of water in the tank.

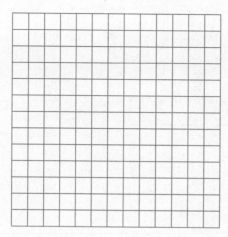

7. Draw a line that represents all possible points. Why does it make sense in this problem situation to connect the points?

8. What are the domain and range of the function?

9. Define a variable to represent each variable quantity. Then use the variables to write an algebraic equation.

10. Identify each constant in the equation from Question 9. What does each constant represent in the problem situation?

This equation you wrote in Question 9 represents a **linear function** because its graph is a line. In a linear function, the dependent variable increases or decreases by a constant amount when the independent variable increases by one unit. This unit rate of change is called the **slope**.

11. What is the unit rate of change, or slope, of the function from Question 9?

12. Graph the linear function represented by the equation $y = 240 - 10x$.

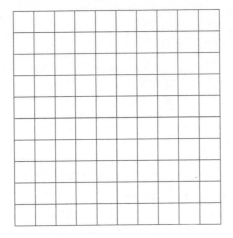

13. What are the domain and range of this linear function?

Problem 2   Water Pumps

Consider the water tank from Problem 1. The homeowner installs a water pump. The water pump starts automatically when the water tank is half full and fills the tank at a rate of 20 gallons per hour. When the water tank is full, the water pump automatically shuts off.

1. The water tank begins full. Create a scatter plot to represent the amount of water in the tank over a 24-hour period.

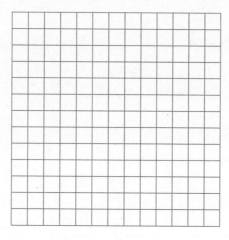

2. Connect the points of the scatter plot. Why does it make sense in this problem situation to connect the points?

3. Describe the shape of the graph.

4. What are the domain and range of this relation?

5. Does the graph have a maximum point or points? If so, what is/are the maximum point(s)?

6. Does the graph have a minimum point or points? If so, what is/are the minimum point(s)?

The maximum and minimum points of a function are called **extreme points** or **extrema**.

7. Use a graphing calculator to graph the equation $y = 120 + |-10x + 120|$ for $0 \leq x \leq 24$. Sketch the graph on the grid.

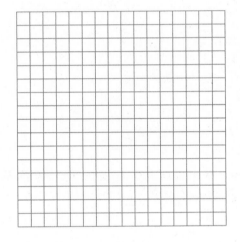

8. How does the graph in Question 7 compare to the graph in Question 1?

The equation $y = 120 + |-10x + 120|$ represents an **absolute value function**. An absolute value function is a function that contains an absolute value expression. The basic absolute value function is $y = |x|$.

9. Draw the vertical line $x = 12$ on the graph in Question 7. What do you notice?

A graph in which a line can be drawn that divides the graph into two parts that are mirror images of one another displays a property called **line symmetry**. The line is called the **line of symmetry**. The reflection of one part of the graph about the line of symmetry is the same as the other part of the graph.

Problem 3

1. Graph each absolute value function. Then identify the domain, range, extrema, and line of symmetry.

   a. $y = |x|$

   Domain:

   Range:

   Extrema:

   Line of symmetry:

   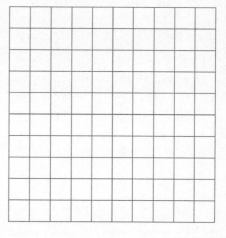

   b. $y = -|2x|$

   Domain:

   Range:

   Extrema:

   Line of symmetry:

   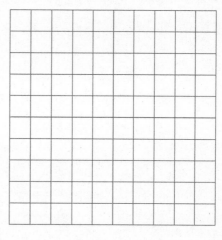

c. $y = 2 + |x + 3|$

Domain:

Range:

Extrema:

Line of symmetry:

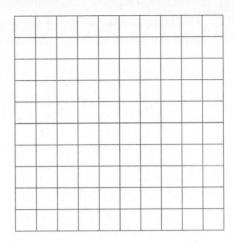

 Be prepared to share your answers with the class.

1.3 Let's Take a Little Trip with Me!
Every Graph Tells a Story

Objectives

In this lesson you will:

- Represent functions using words, tables, equations, and graphs.
- Determine intervals of increase and decrease for a function.
- Interpret the graphs of functions.

Key Terms

- interval of increase
- interval of decrease
- vertical motion
- quadratic function

Problem 1   Gulliver's Travels

The following graph shows the relation between time and Gulliver's distance from home during 1 ten-hour period. Use the graph to answer the following questions.

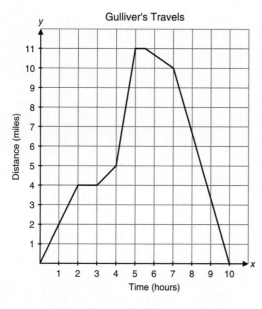

Gulliver's Travels

Distance (miles) vs. Time (hours)

1. Is the relation a function? Explain.

2. Identify any extreme points. What do the extreme points mean in this problem?

3. What is the domain and the range of the relation?

4. How far from home was Gulliver after

    a. two hours?

    b. two and one half hours?

    c. six hours?

    d. eight hours?

    e. ten hours?

5. After how many hours was Gulliver

    a. five miles from home?

    b. ten miles from home?

    c. four miles from home?

6. How far did Gulliver travel during the first two hours of the trip?

7. Consider Gulliver's average speed during the trip.

   a. What was Gulliver's average speed during the first two hours?

   b. What was Gulliver's average speed between seven hours and ten hours?

   c. When was Gulliver moving the fastest? How is this shown on the graph?

   d. What was Gulliver's average speed when he was moving the fastest?

   e. When was Gulliver moving the slowest? How is this shown on the graph?

   f. What was Gulliver's average speed when he was moving the slowest?

8. When was Gulliver moving away from his house? How is this shown on the graph?

9. When was Gulliver moving toward his house? How is this shown on the graph?

10. When was Gulliver standing still? How is this shown on the graph?

As you trace along a graph from left to right, **intervals of increase** are portions of the graph that are increasing. **Intervals of decrease** are portions of the graph that are decreasing.

11. Write a paragraph describing Gulliver's travels. Include each time interval when his speed changed.

Problem 2 Don't Drop the Ball

If two objects of different weights are dropped from the same height, which one will land on the ground first?

This question was explored by the famous mathematician Galileo Galilei. He performed a series of experiments in which he dropped balls of different weights from the Leaning Tower of Pisa. He was able to prove that the weight of an object doesn't matter!

The motion of a dropped object is called **vertical motion** and can be modeled using an algebraic equation.

The following picture shows the height of a tennis ball that was dropped from an initial height of 100 centimeters. A strobe light was used to record the height of the ball every 0.025 seconds.

1. Complete the table using the picture.

Labels	Time	Height
Units	Seconds	Centimeters
	0	
	0.025	

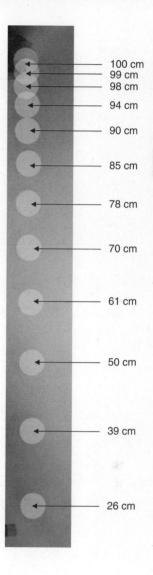

100 cm
99 cm
98 cm
94 cm
90 cm
85 cm
78 cm
70 cm
61 cm
50 cm
39 cm
26 cm

2. Use the table to create a graph showing the relation between time and the height of the tennis ball.

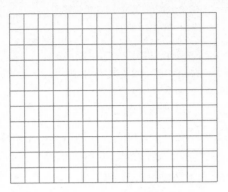

3. Is the relation a function? Explain.

4. Describe the shape of the graph.

5. Does the shape of the graph describe the path of the ball? Explain.

6. Average speed is the ratio of the distance and the time. What was the ball's average speed in centimeters per second

   a. during the first 0.025 seconds?

   b. between 0.15 seconds and 0.175 seconds?

   c. between 0.25 seconds and 0.275 seconds?

7. What do you notice about the average speed of the ball over time? Based on your experience, does this make sense? Explain.

8. Perform the following steps using a graphing calculator.

 a. Enter the equation $y_1 = 100 - 980x^2$.

 b. Set the x-bounds from 0 to 0.325 with an interval of 0.025.

 c. Set the y-bounds from 0 to 100 with an interval of 10.

 d. Turn on the grid.

 e. Graph this function

 What do you notice about this graph and the graph from Question 2?

9. Perform the following steps using a graphing calculator.

 a. Keep the equation $y_1 = 100 - 980x^2$.

 b. Set up a table starting at 0 with intervals of 0.025.

 c. View the table.

 What do you notice about this table and the table from Question 1?

The relation between time and the height of a dropped object is an example of a **quadratic function**. A quadratic function is a function in which the independent variable is raised to a power of two.

Problem 3

For each quadratic function, complete the table and sketch a graph. Then, identify the domain and range, any extreme points and what type they are, intervals of increase and decrease, and the line of symmetry.

1. $y = x^2$

x	y
0	
1	
2	
−1	
−2	

Domain:

Range:

Extreme point:

Interval of increase:

Interval of decrease:

Line of symmetry:

2. $y = -x^2$

x	y
0	
1	
2	
−1	
−2	

Domain:

Range:

Extreme point:

Interval of increase:

Interval of decrease:

Line of symmetry:

3. $y = 2x^2 - 5$

x	y
0	
1	
2	
−1	
−2	

Domain:

Range:

Extreme point:

Interval of increase:

Interval of decrease:

Line of symmetry:

Be prepared to share your answers with the class.

1.4 Building a Better Box
Cubic and Indirect Variation Functions

Objectives

In this lesson you will:

- Represent cubic and indirect variation functions using words, tables, equations, and graphs.
- Interpret the graphs of cubic and indirect variation functions.

Key Terms

- cubic function
- indirect variation function

Problem 1

A company produces liners for planter boxes. To make the liners, a square is cut from each corner of a rectangular copper sheet. The sides are bent to form a box without a top. Cutting different sized squares from the corners results in different sized boxes.

Each rectangular copper sheet is 12 inches by 18 inches. In the diagram, the heavy lines indicate where the cuts are made and the dotted lines represent where the sides are bent.

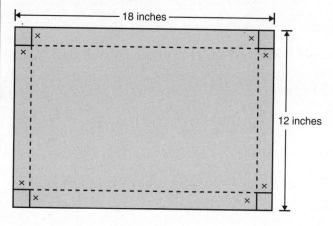

1. What are the height, width, and length of the planter box that result if the length of each side of each corner square is

    a. one inch?

    b. two inches?

    c. four inches?

2. What is the largest size of corner square that can be cut to make a box?

3. Write a formula for the volume of the box.

4. What is the volume of the box that results if the length of each side of the corner square is

    a. one inch?

    b. two inches?

c. four inches?

5. Complete the table using your answers from Questions 1 and 4.

Labels	Side Length of Square	Height of Box	Width of Box	Length of Box	Volume of Box
Units	Inches	Inches	Inches	Inches	Cubic Inches
	0				
	1				
	2				
	3				
	4				
	5				
	6				

6. What is the volume of the box if each side of each corner square is 0 inches or 6 inches? Add these rows to the table in Question 5.

7. Use the table to create a scatter plot for the relation between the side length of the corner squares and the volume of the resulting box.

Take Note

Whenever points are included in a graph to represent endpoints and are not actually part of the graph, we use open points ° to represent them.

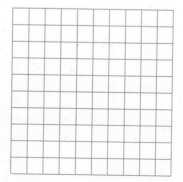

8. Draw a smooth curve connecting the points. Why does it make sense in this problem to connect the points?

9. Is the relation a function? Explain.

10. What is the independent quantity? What is the dependent quantity?

11. Use the graph to estimate the largest possible volume. What size of squares must be cut to make a box with the maximum volume?

12. What are the domain and range of the relation?

13. If the side length of the squares is x inches, what are the height, width, and length of the resulting box?

14. If the side length of the square is x inches, what is the volume of the resulting box?

15. Graph the equation from Question 14 using a graphing calculator. Set the x-bounds of the graph from 0 to 6. What do you notice about this graph and the graph from Question 7?

16. Graph the equation from Question 14 again using a graphing calculator. This time, set the x-bounds of the graph from −10 to 10. Set the y-bounds of the graph from −300 to 300.

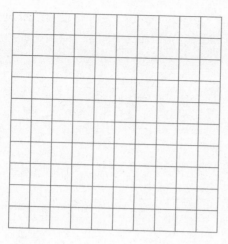

17. Graph the equation $y = 4x^3 - 60x^2 + 216x$ using a graphing calculator. Set the x-bounds of the graph from −10 to 10. Set the y-bounds of the graph from −300 to 300. What do you notice about this graph and the graph from Question 16?

The equations in Questions 14 and 17 are examples of cubic functions. A **cubic function** is a function in which the independent variable is raised to a power of three.

Problem 2

A bucket of paint can cover a flat surface that is 100 square feet with one coat.

1. You are painting a rectangular surface with one can of paint. What is the largest possible length if the width of the rectangular surface is

   a. one foot?

   b. two feet?

   c. five feet?

   d. ten feet?

2. Can the rectangular surface have a length that is more than 100 feet? Explain.

3. Complete the table using your answers from Question 1.

Labels	Width	Length
Units	Feet	Feet
	1	
	2	
	5	
	10	
		5
		2
		1

4. Use the table to create a scatter plot for the relation between width and length.

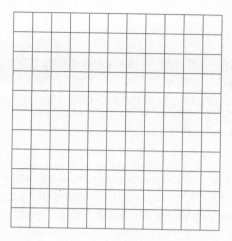

5. Draw a smooth curve connecting the points. Why does it make sense in this problem to connect the points?

6. Is this relation a function? Explain.

7. Is it possible for the width or length of the rectangle to be zero feet? Explain.

8. As the width of the rectangular surface increases, what happens to the length?

9. What are the domain and range of this function?

10. Define variables for the width and the length. Use the variables to write an equation.

11. Graph the equation from Question 10 using a graphing calculator. Set the *x*-bounds of the graph from 0 to 100. Set the *y*-bounds of the graph from 0 to 100. What do you notice about this graph and the graph from Question 4?

The equation in Question 10 is an example of an **indirect variation function.** An indirect variation function is a function where the value of *y* varies indirectly or in the opposite direction to *x*. When *x* increases, *y* decreases proportionally and when *x* decreases, *y* increases proportionally.

Be prepared to share your answers with the class.

How Far Can You See?
How Many Ancestors?

Square Root and Exponential Functions

Objectives

In this lesson you will:

- Represent square root and exponential functions using words, tables, equations, and graphs.
- Interpret the graphs of square root and exponential functions.
- Calculate unit rates of change and average rates of change.

Key Terms

- square root function
- square root
- exponent
- exponential function
- average rate of change

Problem 1   How Far Can You See?

The following graph shows the relation between a person's height above the ground and the maximum distance a person can see across flat ground.

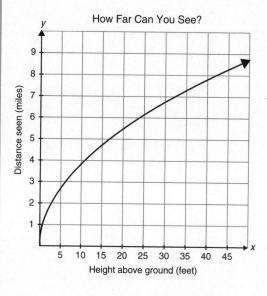

1. Describe the shape of the graph.

© 2009 Carnegie Learning, Inc.

2. Based on the graph, what is the maximum distance that a person can see if they are at a height of

   a. five feet?

   b. 20 feet?

   c. 35 feet?

3. Based on the graph, how high above ground would a person need to be in order to see an object that is at a distance of

   a. six miles?

   b. eight miles?

   c. two miles?

4. Can you use the graph to predict the maximum distance a person could see from the top of a 100-foot building? Explain.

5. Can you use the graph to predict the maximum distance a person could see from an airplane at an altitude of 30,000 feet? Explain.

6. The following graph shows the same relation for heights up to 100 feet. Based on this graph, what is the maximum distance a person could see from the top of a 100-foot building? Compare this answer to you prediction in Question 4.

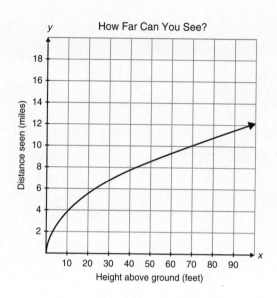

The equation that models this function is $y = \sqrt{1.5x}$, where x is the height above the ground in feet and y is the maximum distance that a person can see in miles. This equation is an example of a **square root function.** A square root function is a function in which the independent variable is contained within a **square root.**

7. Use the equation to answer Question 1. Compare the answers using the equation to the answers using the graph. What do you notice?

8. Use the equation to answer Question 5.

9. What are the advantages and disadvantages of using a graph to make predictions?

10. What are the domain and range of the function $y = \sqrt{1.5x}$?

11. Are the domain and range of the function the same as the domain and range of the problem situation? Explain.

Problem 2   How Many Ancestors?

Did you ever wonder how many relatives you have? You can begin to answer that question by looking at the ancestors you have at each generation. Your parents are one generation from you, your grandparents are two generations from you, and your great-grandparents are three generations from you.

1. How many ancestors do you have

   a. one generation ago?

   b. two generations ago?

   c. three generations ago?

   d. four generations ago?

2. What do you notice about the number of ancestors that you have at each generation?

3. How many ancestors do you have 10 generations ago?

4. How many ancestors do you have 20 generations ago? How did you calculate this number?

5. Let x represent the number of generations ago and let y represent the number of ancestors at that generation. Use the variables to write an equation for the relation between the generation and the number of ancestors.

6. Is this relation a function? Explain.

7. What are the domain and range of the relation?

8. Create a scatter plot of the function for up to 10 generations ago.

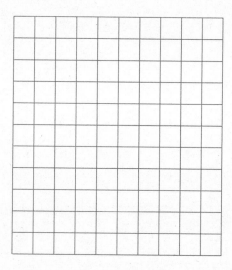

9. Does it make sense to connect the points of the scatter plot? Why or why not?

10. Use the equation to calculate the number of ancestors you have 30 generations ago.

11. A generation is considered to be about 30 years. Using this approximation, during what year were the ancestors from 30 generations ago living? Explain.

12. In the year 1000 there were about 400 million people in the entire world. Is this consistent with your answer in Question 10?

The equation in Question 5 is an example of an **exponential function.** An exponential function is a function where the independent variable is an exponent. The graphs of exponential functions can increase or decrease very rapidly.

Problem 3

1. Complete the first two columns of each table. Then graph the linear function $y = 2x$ and the exponential function $y = 2^x$ on the same grid.

$y = 2x$

x	y	Unit Rate of Change
1		
2		
3		
4		
5		

$y = 2^x$

x	y	Unit Rate of Change
1		
2		
3		
4		
5		

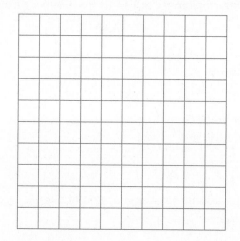

2. Compare the graphs of the linear function $y = 2x$ and the exponential function $y = 2^x$.

3. The slope, or unit rate of change, is the ratio of the change in the dependent variable to a change in the independent variable of one unit. Complete the third column of each table in Question 1.

4. Describe the differences in the unit rates of change for the linear function $y = 2x$ and the exponential function $y = 2^x$.

The **average rate of change** is the ratio of the change in the dependent variable to the change in the independent variable, or $\dfrac{y_2 - y_1}{x_2 - x_1}$.

For example, the average rate of change for $y = 2x$ from 1 to 5 is $\dfrac{10 - 2}{5 - 1} = \dfrac{8}{4} = 2$.

5. What is the average rate of change for $y = 2x$ from 1 to 4? from 2 to 4?

6. What is the average rate of change for $y = 2^x$ from 1 to 5? from 2 to 4?

7. What can you conclude about the average rates of change and the unit rates of change for linear functions?

8. What can you conclude about the average rates of change and the unit rates of change for exponential functions?

 Be prepared to share your answers with the class.

2 Algebraic Functions

About 1.4 billion cotton T-shirts, with a retail value of about $20 billion, are sold annually in North America. Several thousand T-shirt retailers do business on the Internet alone. You will use arithmetic sequences to calculate the cost of ordering T-shirts in bulk.

2

2.1 Functional Function: *F* of *x* it is!
Functional Notation

Objectives

In this lesson you will:

- Write functions using functional notation.
- Evaluate functions using functional notation.
- Identify independent and dependent values using tables, graphs, and equations.

Key Terms

- functional notation
- evaluating a function

Functional notation is a way of representing functions algebraically. Function notation makes it easier to recognize the independent and dependent variables in an equation. The function $f(x)$ is read as "*f* of *x*" and indicates that *x* is the independent variable.

Consider the equation $c = 8s + 15$, where the independent variable *s* represents the number of shirts ordered and the dependent variable *c* represents the cost of the order. The equation can be written using functional notation as $f(s) = 8s + 15$. The cost, defined by *f*, is a function of *s*, the number of shirts ordered.

The process of calculating the value of a function for a specific value of the independent variable is called **evaluating a function.** For example, the cost of ordering 4 shirts can be calculated by evaluating the function at $s = 4$.

This is written as $f(4)$ and read as "*f* of 4."

To evaluate, substitute 4 for *s* in the rule $f(s) = 8s + 15$.

$f(4) = 8(4) + 15 = 32 + 15 = 47$

$f(4) = 47$

Problem 1   Functions as Equations

1. The function $f(s) = 8s + 15$ represents the cost of ordering s shirts. What are the domain and range of the function?

2. Use the equation $f(s) = 8s + 15$ to evaluate the function at each value. Explain what each means in terms of the problem.

    a. $f(7)$

    b. $f(100)$

    c. $f(11)$

    d. $f(0)$

    e. $f(2.5)$

3. Evaluating the function *f* at 4 is written as $f(4) = 47$, and read as "the value of the function *f* at 4 is 47" or "*f* of 4 is 47." How would each evaluation in Question 1 be read?

4. Calculate the value of *x* that makes each equation true. Explain what each means in terms of the problem.

a. $f(x) = 55$

b. $f(x) = 175$

c. $f(x) = 151$

Problem 2   Functions as Tables

The function $h(a)$ represents the average height of boys that are a years old.

Boy's Age	Average Height in Inches
6 months	26
12 months	30
18 months	34
2 years	36
3 years	39
4 years	42
5 years	44
6 years	47
7 years	49
8 years	51
9 years	53
10 years	55
11 years	57
12 years	59
13 years	61

1. Use the table to evaluate the function at each value. Explain what each means in terms of the problem.

   a. $h(7)$

   b. $h(1.5)$

   c. $h(11)$

   d. $h(12.5)$

© 2009 Carnegie Learning, Inc.

2. Calculate the value of *a* that makes each equation true. Explain what each means in terms of the problem.

a. $h(a) = 61$

b. $h(a) = 36$

c. $h(a) = 53$

d. $h(a) = 45$

Problem 3   Functions as Graphs

The function *d*(*t*) represents Gulliver's distance from home after *t* hours.

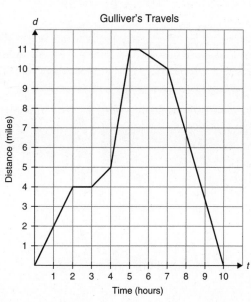

1. Use the graph to evaluate the function at each value. Explain what each means in terms of the problem.

   a. $d(2)$

   b. $d(5)$

   c. $d(2.9)$

   d. $d(10)$

2. Calculate the value of t that makes each equation true. Explain what each means in terms of the problem.

   a. $d(t) = 2$

   b. $d(t) = 5$

   c. $d(t) = 4$

   d. $d(t) = 0$

Be prepared to share your solutions and methods.

2.2 Numbers in a Row!
Introduction to Sequences

Objectives

In this lesson you will:

- Define a mathematical sequence as a function with domain of the counting numbers.
- Describe sequences using words, numbers, diagrams, and figures.
- Define numerical sequences using an explicit formula for the nth or general term.
- Define numerical sequences using recursive formulas.

Key Terms

- mathematical sequence
- term
- finite sequence
- infinite sequence
- explicit or general term formula
- recursive formula

A **mathematical sequence**, or just a **sequence**, is a number pattern or a list of numbers. Each number of the sequence is called a **term**.

The ability to recognize patterns, especially in numbers, is very important. Sometimes, the pattern is easy to notice.

$$1, 3, 5, 7, 9, \underline{\hphantom{xxx}}, \underline{\hphantom{xxx}}, \ldots$$

Sometimes, the pattern is more difficult to recognize.

$$0, 1, 5, 14, 30, 55, \underline{\hphantom{xxx}}, \underline{\hphantom{xxx}}, \ldots$$

You can use a pattern to calculate a particular term of a sequence. As with recognizing a pattern, sometimes calculating a term is easy.

$$4, 8, 12, 16, \ldots, \underbrace{\underline{\hphantom{xxx}}}_{\text{10th term}}, \ldots$$

However, sometimes it may be difficult to calculate a term.

$$1, 1, 2, 3, 5, 8, 13, \ldots, \underbrace{\underline{\hphantom{xxx}}}_{\text{10th term}}, \ldots$$

Sequences can be described by a list of numbers, diagrams, or other figures.

1. For each sequence, describe the pattern. Then determine the next two figures and the next two corresponding terms of the sequence.

   a.

   Figures:

   Number of
   points: 1   3   6   10

   b. Each figure is made from toothpicks.

   Figures: □   □□   □□□

   Number of
   toothpicks: 4   7   10

   c.

   Figures:

   Number of
   segments   1   3   6

2. For each sequence, describe the pattern. Then determine the next two terms and the tenth term.

   a. 1, 4, 9, 16,   ,   , ... , , ...

                                 10th term

b. 2, 4, 6, 8,   ,   , ... , ⌣ , ...

10th term

c. 3, 7, 11, 15,   ,   , ... , ⌣ , ...

10th term

d. $\frac{1}{4}$, $\frac{1}{8}$, $\frac{1}{16}$, $\frac{1}{32}$,   ,   , ... , ⌣ , ...

10th term

Sequences are often represented as a_1, a_2, a_3, a_4, ... , a_n, ... , where the subscript represents the position of the term in the sequence. For example, a_{100} is the one hundredth term of a sequence.

A **finite sequence** is a sequence with a finite number of terms. For example, the sequence 2, 4, 6, 8, 10, 12 is a finite sequence. An **infinite sequence** is a sequence with an infinite number of terms. For example, the sequence 2, 4, 6, 8, 10, 12, ... is an infinite sequence.

3. For each sequence, describe the pattern. Then write a formula to calculate the nth term.

a. 10, 20, 30, 40, ... , ⌣ , ...

nth term

b. 2, 4, 8, 16, ... , ⌣ , ...

nth term

c. 23, 31, 39, 47, ... , ⌣ , ...

nth term

d. 1, $\frac{1}{2}$, $\frac{1}{3}$, $\frac{1}{4}$, ... , ⌣ , ...

nth term

Problem 2   Sequences as Functions

1. Use the sequence from Problem 1 Question 2(a) to complete the table.

Term Number	Value of Term
1	1
2	4
3	
4	
5	
10	
n	

a. Describe how to calculate the value of each term from the term number.

b. Write a function $f(n)$ to calculate the nth term of the sequence.

c. What are the domain and range of $f(n)$?

d. Is $f(1.5)$ defined? Explain.

2. Use the sequence from Problem 1 Question 2(b) to complete the table.

Term Number	Value of Term
1	2
2	
3	
4	
5	
10	
n	

a. Describe how to calculate the value of each term from the term number.

b. Write a function $g(n)$ to calculate the nth term of the sequence.

c. What are the domain and range of $g(n)$?

d. Calculate each term of the sequence.

a_{20}

a_{25}

a_{50}

a_n

3. Use the sequence from Problem 1 Question 2(c) to answer each question.

a. Describe how to calculate the value of each term from the term number.

b. Write a function $h(n)$ to calculate the nth term of the sequence.

c. What are the domain and range of $h(n)$?

d. Calculate each term of the sequence.

a_{20}

a_{25}

a_{50}

a_n

4. What is the domain of a function used to model a sequence?

5. What is the range of a function used to model a sequence?

Problem 3   Explicit Formulas

In Problems 2 and 3 you wrote formulas to calculate a_n, the value of a term of a sequence, using n, the term number. This formula, called a **general term formula** or **explicit formula**, defines all terms of a sequence in terms of the term number.

1. Use each explicit formula to generate the first four terms and the tenth term of the sequence.

  a. $a_n = 3n + 5$

  b. $a_n = n^2 + n$

  c. $a_n = \dfrac{2}{n}$

  d. $a_n = 5\left(\dfrac{1}{2}\right)^n$

2. Write an explicit formula for each sequence.

  a. 2, 4, 8, 16, …

  b. 4, 9, 14, 19, …

  c. 5, 12, 19, 26, …

  d. 2, 5, 10, 17, …

Problem 4 Recursive Formulas

For some sequences, it is easier to describe the pattern in terms of what operations are performed to calculate the next term from the previous term. A **recursive formula** is a formula for defining all terms of a sequence in terms of the previous terms.

For example, consider the sequence 10, 15, 20, 25, ... Each term of the sequence is calculated by adding 5 to the previous term. The sequence can be defined recursively as:

$a_1 = 10, a_n = a_{n-1} + 5$

Notice that a recursive formula has two parts: the first term and a formula for calculating each term.

1. Use each recursive formula to generate the first four terms of the sequence.

   a. $a_1 = 3, a_n = 2a_{n-1}$

   b. $a_1 = 23, a_n = a_{n-1} + 8$

   c. $a_1 = 1, a_n = 3a_{n-1} - 2$

   d. $a_1 = 7, a_n = 3a_{n-1} - 2$

   e. $a_1 = 2, a_n = (a_{n-1})^2$

© 2009 Carnegie Learning, Inc.

2. Write a recursive formula for each sequence.

   a. 3, 7, 11, 15, …

   b. 3, 7, 15, 31, …

   c. 1, 2, 5, 26, …

   d. $\frac{2}{3}$, 1, $\frac{4}{3}$, $\frac{5}{3}$, …

Be prepared to share your solutions and methods.

2.3 Adding or Multiplying
Arithmetic and Geometric Sequence

Objectives

In this lesson you will:

- Determine the initial term and the common difference for arithmetic sequences.
- Define arithmetic sequences using explicit and recursive formulas.
- Determine the initial term and the common ratio for geometric sequences.
- Define geometric sequences using explicit and recursive formulas.

Key Terms

- arithmetic sequence
- common difference
- geometric sequence
- common ratio

Problem I   Arithmetic Sequences

1. Calculate the first four terms of each sequence.

   a. $a_n = 5n$

   $a_1 =$ $a_2 =$ $a_3 =$ $a_4 =$

   b. $a_1 = 2$ $a_n = a_{n-1} + 3$

   $a_1 =$ $a_2 =$ $a_3 =$ $a_4 =$

   c. $a_n = 2n + 4$

   $a_1 =$ $a_2 =$ $a_3 =$ $a_4 =$

   d. $a_1 = 4$ $a_n = a_{n-1} - 3$

   $a_1 =$ $a_2 =$ $a_3 =$ $a_4 =$

2. Write a recursive formula for each sequence.

   a. 10, 20, 30, 40, ... $a_1 =$ $a_n =$

   b. −3, −5, −7, −9, ... $a_1 =$ $a_n =$

   c. 1, 0, −1, −2, ... $a_1 =$ $a_n =$

   d. 2, 9, 16, 23, ... $a_1 =$ $a_n =$

3. Write an explicit formula for each sequence.

   a. 4, 8, 12, 16, …

   b. 3, 5, 7, 9, …

   c. 2, 9, 16, 23, …

   d. 3, 0, −3, −6, …

4. What is similar about the sequences in Questions 1 through 3?

An **arithmetic sequence** is a sequence in which each term is calculated from the preceding term by adding a constant. This constant is called the **common difference**. An arithmetic sequence is defined by the initial term a_1 and the common difference, d.

For example, consider the sequence that represents the cost of ordering shirts: 23, 31, 39, 47, … . The term number represents the number of shirts ordered and the value of the term represents the cost of ordering that many shirts. The initial term is 23. This represents the cost of ordering 1 shirt. The common difference is 8. For each additional shirt that is ordered, the cost is increasing by $8.

5. Write an explicit formula for the sequence that represents the cost of ordering shirts.

6. Write the formula from Question 5 as a function.

7. What is the y-intercept of the function? Is this the same as the initial term of the sequence? Why or why not?

8. Generate the first four terms of each arithmetic sequence. Then write a recursive formula and an explicit formula.

   a. Initial term of 3 and common difference of 2

   b. Initial term of 3 and common difference of -2

   c. Initial term of 10 and common difference of -3

   d. Initial term of a_1 and common difference of d.

9. For each arithmetic sequence, identify the common difference. Then write a recursive formula and an explicit formula.

   a. 3, 6, 9, 12, ...

   b. 3, 5, 7, 9, ...

c. 12, 7, 2, −3, …

d. 1, 9, 17, 25, …

e. $\frac{1}{2}, -\frac{1}{2}, -\frac{3}{2}, -\frac{5}{2}, …$

Problem 2 Geometric Sequences

1. Calculate the first four terms of each sequence.

a. $a_n = 3 \cdot 2^{n-1}$

$a_1 =$ \qquad $a_2 =$ \qquad $a_3 =$ \qquad $a_4 =$

Take Note

$a^0 = 1$ by definition of a zero exponent.

b. $a_1 = 2$ $a_n = 3a_{n-1}$

$a_1 =$ \qquad $a_2 =$ \qquad $a_3 =$ \qquad $a_4 =$

c. $a_n = -2\left(\frac{1}{2}\right)^{n-1}$

$a_1 =$ \qquad $a_2 =$ \qquad $a_3 =$ \qquad $a_4 =$

d. $a_1 = -1$ $a_n = -2a_{n-1}$

$a_1 =$ \qquad $a_2 =$ \qquad $a_3 =$ \qquad $a_4 =$

2. Write a recursive formula for each sequence.

a. 1, 10, 100, 1000, … a_1 \qquad a_n

b. $3, -1, \frac{1}{3}, -\frac{1}{9}, …$ a_1 \qquad a_n

c. $3, 2, \frac{4}{3}, \frac{8}{3}, …$ a_1 \qquad a_n

d. 10, 1, 0.1, 0.01, … a_1 \qquad a_n

3. Write an explicit formula for each sequence.

   a. 1, 2, 4, 8, …

   b. $\frac{1}{2}$, $-\frac{1}{4}$, $\frac{1}{8}$, $-\frac{1}{16}$, …

   c. 2, −6, 18, −54, …

   d. 11, 1.1, 0.11, 0.011, …

4. What is similar about the sequences in Questions 1 through 3?

A **geometric sequence** is a sequence in which each term is calculated from the preceding term by multiplying by a constant. This constant is called the **common ratio**. A geometric sequence is defined by the initial term, g_1, and the common ratio, r.

5. Generate the first four terms of each geometric sequence. Then write a recursive formula and an explicit formula.

   a. Initial term of −2 and common ratio of 3

   b. Initial term of 1 and common ratio of $\frac{1}{2}$

   c. Initial term of 100 and common ratio of $\frac{1}{4}$

   d. Initial term of g_1 and common ratio of r

6. For each geometric sequence, identify the common ratio. Then write a recursive formula and an explicit formula.

   a. 1, 6, 36, 216, ...

   b. $\frac{1}{4}$, $-\frac{1}{2}$, 1, -2

   c. 12, 6, 3, $\frac{3}{2}$, ...

   d. $\frac{9}{4}$, $-\frac{3}{2}$, 1, $-\frac{2}{3}$, ...

Problem 3   Classifying Sequences

Classify each sequence as arithmetic, geometric, or neither.

For each arithmetic sequence, identify the common difference. Then write a recursive formula and an explicit formula.

For each geometric sequence, identify the common ratio. Then write a recursive formula and an explicit formula.

1. $\dfrac{1}{3}, \dfrac{2}{3}, \dfrac{4}{3}, \dfrac{8}{3}, \ldots$

2. 12, 14.5, 17, 19.5, …

3. 1, 3, 7, 15, …

4. 12, 8, 4, 0

5. 0, 3, 8, 15, …

6. −1, 5, −25, 125, …

Be prepared to share your solutions and methods.

2.4 Home, Home on the Domains and Ranges

Domains and Ranges of Algebraic Functions

Objective

In this lesson you will:

- Determine the domains and ranges of functions.

Problem 1

A company makes boxes of various sizes. Each box is a rectangular prism with a height of 8 inches and a volume of 1200 cubic inches.

1. Let x represent the width of a box. Write a function $f(x)$ to model the length of the box.

2. What type of function is $f(x)$?

3. Use $f(x)$ to calculate the following.

    a. What is the length of a box with a width of 10 inches?

    b. $f(15)$

c. $f(1)$

d. What is the width of a box with a length of 5 inches?

e. What is the value of x if $f(x) = 100$?

f. What is the value of x if $f(x) = 2$?

g. Is it possible to make a box so that the length and width are equal? If so, what is the common value of the length and width?

4. Enter the values from Question 3 in the following table.

Labels		
Units		
Expression		

5. Create a scatter plot of the function on the grid shown.

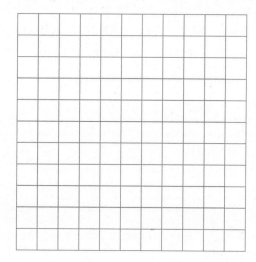

6. Draw a curve that represents all possible lengths and widths. Why does it make sense to connect the points of the scatter plot?

2

7. What happens to the length as the width gets very large?

8. Is it possible to make a box with a length of zero inches? How do you know based on the problem situation? How do you know based on the graph?

9. What happens to the length as the width gets very small?

10. Is it possible to make a box with a width of zero inches? How do you know based on the problem situation? How do you know based on the graph?

11. Does the graph intersect the *x*- or *y*-axis? What does this mean in terms of the problem situation?

12. What are the domain and range of *f*(*x*) in this problem situation?

Problem 2

1. Use the function from Problem 1 to calculate the following.

   a. $f(-15)$ **b.** $f(-1.5)$

   c. $f(-25)$ **d.** $f(x) = -5$

   e. $f(x) = -10$ **f.** $f(x) = -1$

2. Do the values from Question 1 make sense in terms of the problem situation? Explain.

3. Graph the function using a graphing calculator. Set the *x*-bounds of the graph from -100 to 100.

4. How is the graph in Question 3 different from the graph in Problem 1 Question 5? How is it similar?

5. Is *x* ever equal to 0? Explain using the graph and the function.

6. Is $f(x)$ ever equal to 0? Explain using the graph and the function.

7. Examining your graph, what appears to be happening as *x* approaches zero from the right? from the left?

8. Does the graph intersect the *x*- or *y*-axis? Explain.

9. What are the domain and range of the function?

Problem 3

Graph each function. Then identify the type of function and determine the domain and range of the function.

1. $g(x) = 2x - 3$

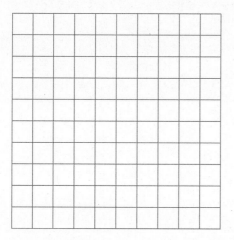

Type of function:

Domain:

Range:

2. $f(x) = \sqrt{2x}$

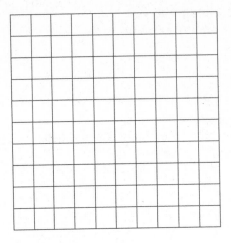

Type of function:

Domain:

Range:

3. $h(x) = |x - 1|$

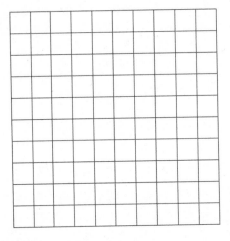

Type of function:

Domain:

Range:

4. $g(x) = -2x^2$

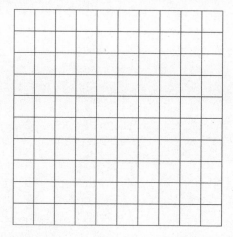

Type of function:

Domain:

Range:

 Be prepared to share your solutions and methods.

2

2.5 Rocket Man
Extrema and Symmetry

Objectives

In this lesson you will:

- Determine *x*- and *y*-intercepts of graphs.
- Calculate extreme points of graphs.
- Identify lines of symmetry of graphs.

Problem 1

The graph shows the horizontal distance from launch and the height of a rocket.

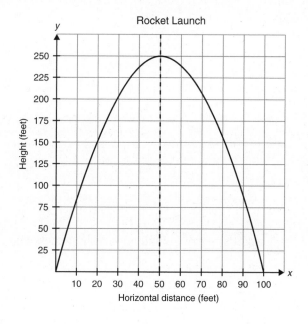

Rocket Launch

2

Horizontal distance (feet)

Height (feet)

© 2009 Carnegie Learning, Inc.

1. What is the height of the rocket when the horizontal distance from launch is

   a. 20 feet?

   b. 40 feet?

   c. 90 feet?

2. What is the horizontal distance of the rocket from launch when the height is

   a. 125 feet?

   b. 200 feet?

   c. 300 feet?

3. What is the rocket's horizontal distance from launch when it is on the ground?

4. What is the maximum height of the rocket? What is the rocket's horizontal distance from launch when it is at this maximum height?

5. What term is used to describe the point from Question 4? Why?

6. For what values of x is the graph increasing? Decreasing?

7. Is the graph increasing or decreasing when x = 50?

8. Draw a vertical line at x = 50. What term is used to describe this line? Why?

9. Examine your answers to each part of Questions 2 and 3. What do you notice about your answers and the line you drew in Question 8?

10. Do all functions have **extreme points**? Do all functions have **lines of symmetry**? Explain.

11. Can a function have a line of symmetry but not an extreme point? If so, describe the function.

12. Can a function have an extreme point but not a line of symmetry? If so, describe the function.

Problem 2

For each function:

- Sketch a graph.

- Determine the domain and range.

- Determine the x- and y-intercept(s) and label each on the graph.

- Determine any vertical or horizontal lines of symmetry and draw each on the graph.

- Determine all extreme points and label each on the graph.

1. $f(x) = |2x - 4|$

Domain:

Range:

x-intercept(s):

y-intercept(s):

Line of symmetry:

Extreme point:

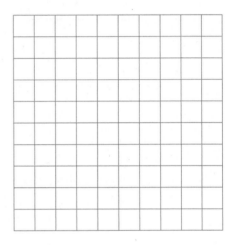

2. $f(x) = x^2 - 6x - 27$

Domain:

Range:

x-intercept(s):

y-intercept(s):

Line of symmetry:

Extreme point:

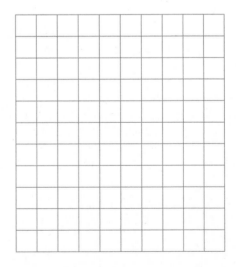

3. $f(x) = 2 + \sqrt{x}$

Domain:

Range:

x-intercept(s):

y-intercept(s):

Line of symmetry:

Extreme point:

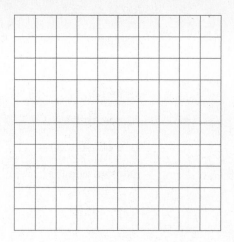

4. $f(x) = 5x - 6$

Domain:

Range:

x-intercept(s):

y-intercept(s):

Line of symmetry:

Extreme point:

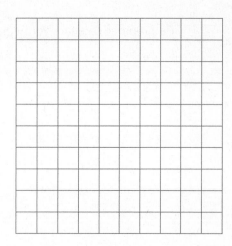

5. $f(x) = \dfrac{20}{x}$

Domain:

Range:

x-intercept(s):

y-intercept:

Line of symmetry:

Extreme point:

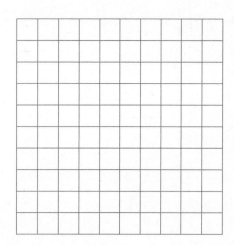

6. $f(x) = x^3 - x$

Domain:

Range:

x-intercept(s):

y-intercept(s):

Line of symmetry:

Extreme point:

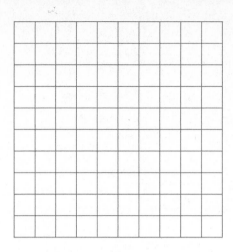

Be prepared to share your solutions and methods.

2.6 Changing Change
Rates of Change of Functions

Objectives

In this lesson you will:

- Calculate average rates of change of functions.
- Understand the relationship between average rate of change and slope.
- Describe the average rates of change for different functions.

Key Term

- average rate of change

Problem 1

The graph of the function $g(x) = x + 3$ is shown on the grid. The points $(1, 4)$ and $(-4, -1)$ are labeled.

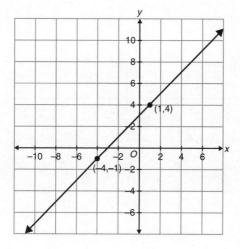

1. What type of function is $g(x)$?

2. Complete the following table.

   a. Locate three other points and add these points to the table.

   b. Calculate the change in the x-values of consecutive points, Δx, by subtracting the x-value in the preceding row from the x-value in the current row.

   c. Calculate the change in the y-values of consecutive points, Δy, by subtracting the y-value in the preceding row from the y-value in the current row.

   d. Calculate the average rate of change between consecutive points, $\frac{\Delta y}{\Delta x}$.

x	y	Δx	Δy	$\frac{\Delta y}{\Delta x}$
1	4			
−4	−1	−5	−5	1
−3				

3. What do you notice about the average rates of change for g(x)?

4. Complete the table for the linear function f(x) = −2x + 1.

x	y	Δx	Δy	$\frac{\Delta y}{\Delta x}$
1				
2				
−3				
0				
−2				

5. What do you notice about the average rates of change for f(x)?

6. What can you conclude about the average rates of change for linear functions?

7. What is another term for the average rate of change for a linear function?

Problem 2

The graph of the function $k(x) = |2x - 1|$ is shown on the grid. The points (1, 1), (3, 5), (−1, 3), and (−3, 7) are labeled.

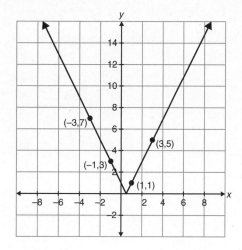

1. What type of function is $k(x)$?

2. Calculate the average rate of change between the two leftmost points.

3. Calculate the average rate of change between the two rightmost points.

4. What can you conclude about the average rate of change for the right part of the graph?

5. What can you conclude about the average rate of change for the left part of the graph?

6. What can you conclude about the average rates of change for absolute value functions?

Problem 3

The graph of the function $p(x) = x^2$ is shown on the grid. The points (1, 1) and (4, 16) are labeled.

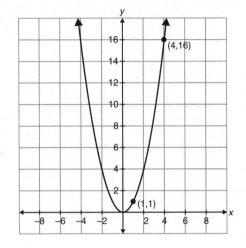

1. What type of function is $p(x)$?

2. Calculate the average rate of change between the points (1, 1) and (4, 16).

3. Draw a line between the points (1, 1) and (4, 16). What is the slope of the line?

4. How does the slope of the line compare to the average rate of change between the two points?

5. Evaluate $p(x)$ for $x = 2$. Represent the result as an ordered pair.

6. Calculate each average rate of change.

   a. Between the point from Question 5 and (1, 1)

   a. Between the point from Question 5 and (4, 16)

7. Draw a line between the point from Question 5 and (1, 1). Draw another line between the point from Question 5 and (4, 16). What is the slope of each line?

8. How does the slope of each line compare to the average rate of change between the two points?

9. What do you think will be true about the average rate of change between two points to the left of the minimum point?

10. What can you conclude about the average rates of change for quadratic functions?

Problem 4

The graph of the function $q(x) = 2^x$ is shown on the grid. The points (1, 2) and (4, 16) are labeled.

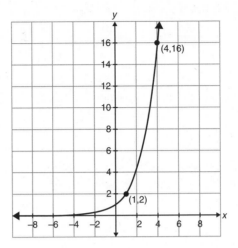

1. What type of function is $q(x)$?

2. Calculate the average rate of change between the points (1, 2) and (4, 16).

3. Draw a line between the points (1, 2) and (4, 16). What is the slope of the line?

4. How does the slope of the line compare to the average rate of change between the two points?

5. Evaluate $q(x)$ for $x = 3$. Represent the result as an ordered pair.

6. Calculate each average rate of change.

    a. Between the point from Question 5 and (1, 2).

    b. Between the point from Question 5 and (4, 16).

7. Draw a line between the point from Question 5 and (1, 2). Draw another line between the point from Question 5 and (4, 16). What is the slope of each line?

8. How does the slope of each line compare to the average rate of change between the two points?

9. What can you conclude about the average rates of change for exponential functions?

Problem 5

Complete the table to summarize the properties of several basic functions.

Function Type	Linear	Absolute Value	Quadratic
Equation of Basic Function			
Graph			
Domain and Range			
Extrema			
Intervals of Increasing and Decreasing			
Vertical Line of Symmetry			

Function Type	Cubic	Indirect Variation
Equation of Basic Function		
Graph		
Domain and Range		
Extrema		
Intervals of Increasing and Decreasing		
Vertical Line of Symmetry		

Function Type	Square Root	Exponential
Equation of Basic Function		
Graph		
Domain and Range		
Extrema		
Intervals of Increasing and Decreasing		
Vertical Line of Symmetry		

 Be prepared to share your solutions and methods.

3 Logic

Riding a bicycle is a skill which, once learned, is rarely forgotten. What's more, bicycles are enough alike that if you can ride one bike, you can pretty much ride them all. This is an example of inductive reasoning, which is applying knowledge and experience learned in one situation to another situation. You will learn about inductive reasoning and how to apply it to mathematical problems.

3

3.1 A Little Dash of Logic
Two Methods of Logical Reasoning

Objectives

In this lesson you will:

- Define inductive reasoning and deductive reasoning.
- Identify methods of reasoning.
- Compare and contrast methods of reasoning.
- Create examples using inductive and deductive reasoning.

Key Terms

- inductive reasoning
- deductive reasoning

Problem 1

1. Emma is watching her big sister do homework. She notices the following:

   - $4^2 = 4 \times 4$
   - nine cubed is equal to nine times nine times nine
   - 10 to the fourth power is equal to four factors of 10 multiplied together

   Emma concludes that raising a number to a power is the same as multiplying the number by itself as many times as indicated by the power. How did Emma reach this conclusion?

2. Ricky read that exponents mean repeated multiplication. He had to enter seven to the fourth power in a calculator but could not find the exponent button. So, he entered $7 \times 7 \times 7 \times 7$ instead. How did Ricky reach this conclusion?

3. Contrast the reasoning used by Emma and Ricky.

4. Was Emma's conclusion correct? Was Ricky's conclusion correct?

5. Jennifer's mother is a writing consultant. She was paid $900 for a ten-hour job and $1980 for a twenty two-hour job.

   a. How much does Jennifer's mother charge per hour?

   b. To answer Question 5(a), did you start with a general rule and make a conclusion or did you start with specific information and create a general rule?

6. Your friend Aaron tutors elementary school students. He tells you that the job pays $8.25 per hour.

   a. How much does Aaron earn if he works 4 hours?

   b. To answer Question 6(a), did you start with a general rule and make a conclusion or did you start with specific information and create a general rule?

Problem 2

The ability to use information to reason and make conclusions is very important in life and in mathematics. This lesson focuses on two methods of reasoning. You can construct the vocabulary for each type of reasoning by thinking about what prefixes, root words, and suffixes mean.

Look at the following information. Remember that a prefix is a beginning of a word. A suffix is an ending of a word.

- *in*—a prefix that can mean *toward* or *up to*
- *de*—a prefix that can mean *down from*
- *duc*—a base or root word meaning *to lead* and often *to think*, from the Latin word *duco*
- *-tion*—a suffix that forms a noun meaning *the act of*

1. Form a word that means "the act of thinking down from."

2. Form a word that means "the act of thinking toward or up to."

Inductive reasoning is reasoning that involves using specific examples to make a conclusion. Many times in life you must make generalizations about observations or patterns and apply these generalizations to unfamiliar situations. For example, you learn how to ride a bike by falling down, getting back up, and trying again. Eventually, you are able to balance on your own. After learning to ride your own bike, you can apply that knowledge and experience to ride an unfamiliar bike.

Deductive reasoning is reasoning that involves using a general rule to make a conclusion. For example, you learn the rule for which direction to turn a screwdriver: "righty tighty, lefty loosey." If you want to unscrew a screw, you apply the rule and turn counterclockwise.

3. Look back at Problem 1. Who used inductive reasoning?

4. Who used deductive reasoning?

Problem 3

1. Your best friend reads a newspaper article that states that use of tobacco greatly increases the risk of cancer. He then notices that his neighbor Matilda smokes. He is concerned that Matilda has a high risk of cancer.

a. What is the specific information in this problem?

b. What is the general information in this problem?

c. What is the conclusion in this problem?

d. Did your friend use inductive or deductive reasoning to make the conclusion? Explain.

e. Is your friend's conclusion correct? Explain.

© 2009 Carnegie Learning, Inc.

2. Molly returned from a trip to London and tells you, "It rains every day in England!" She explains that it rained each of the five days she was there.

   a. What is the specific information in this problem?

   b. What is the general information in this problem?

   c. What is the conclusion in this problem?

   d. Did Molly use inductive or deductive reasoning to make the conclusion? Explain.

   e. Is Molly's conclusion correct? Explain.

3. You take detailed notes in history class and math class. A classmate is going to miss biology class tomorrow to attend a field trip. His biology teacher asks him if he knows someone in class who always takes detailed notes. He gives your name to the teacher. The biology teacher suggests he borrow your biology notes because he concludes that they will be detailed.

   a. What conclusion did your classmate make? Why?

   b. What type of reasoning did your classmate use? Explain.

   c. What conclusion did the biology teacher make? Why?

d. What type of reasoning did the biology teacher use? Explain.

e. Will your classmate's conclusion always be true? Will the biology teacher's conclusion always be true? Explain.

4. The first four numbers in a sequence are 4, 15, 26, and 37.

   a. What is the next number in the sequence? How did you calculate the next number?

   b. What types of reasoning did you use and in what order to make the conclusion?

5. Write a short note to a friend explaining induction and deduction. Include definitions of both terms and examples that are very easy to understand.

© 2009 Carnegie Learning, Inc.

Problem 4

There are two reasons why a conclusion may be false. Either the assumed information is false or the argument is not valid.

1. Derek tells his little brother that it will not rain for the next thirty days because he "knows everything." Why is this conclusion false?

2. Two lines are not parallel so the lines must intersect. Why is this conclusion false?

3. Write an example of a conclusion that is false because the assumed information is false.

4. Write an example of a conclusion that is false because the argument is not valid.

Be prepared to share your solutions and methods.

3.2 What's Your Conclusion?
Hypotheses, Conclusions, Conditional Statements, Counterexamples, Direct and Indirect Arguments

Objectives

In this lesson you will:
- Define a conditional statement.
- Identify the hypothesis and conclusion of a conditional statement.
- Construct direct and indirect arguments.

Key Terms
- conditional statement
- hypothesis
- conclusion
- proof by contrapositive
- direct argument
- counterexample
- indirect argument

Problem I

Read each pair of statements. Then write a valid conclusion.

1. Statement: Melanie's school guidance counselor tells her that if she applies for a scholarship, she will have a chance to receive it.
   Statement: Melanie applies for a scholarship.
   Conclusion:

2. Statement: If it rains, the baseball game will be cancelled.
   Statement: It rains.
   Conclusion:

3. Statement: If Suzanne misses the application deadline for the Vocational Training School, she will not be admitted.
   Statement: Suzanne missed the application deadline.
   Conclusion:

4. Statement: Marvin will know whether he enjoys waltz lessons if he attends his first waltz lesson.
   Statement: Marvin attended his first waltz lesson.
   Conclusion:

5. Statement: If having the most experience as a nuclear engineer had been the main requirement, then Olga would have gotten the job.
   Statement: Olga did not get the job.
   Conclusion:

Problem 2

Read each statement and conclusion. Then write the additional statement required to reach the conclusion.

1. Statement: If no evidence can be found linking a suspect to the scene of a crime, then the suspect will be found innocent.

   Statement:

   Conclusion: Therefore, the suspect was found innocent.

2. Statement: If the community service program chooses the litter removal project, then Mayor Elder will have the carnival in this neighborhood.

   Statement:

   Conclusion: Therefore, the community service program did not choose the litter removal project.

3. Statement: If clematis flowers are to survive, then they need sunlight.
   Statement:
   Conclusion: Therefore, the clematis flowers died.

4. Statement: The Secret Service will be at the dinner if the President shows up.

   Statement:
   Conclusion: Therefore, the President did not show up at the dinner.

5. Statement: If
   Statement: You have your umbrella.
   Conclusion: Therefore, it must have been raining.

6. Statement: If

   Statement: You ate a good breakfast.
   Conclusion: Therefore, you will not be hungry before lunch.

7. Statement: If

   Statement: You did your math homework.
   Conclusion: Therefore, your teacher is happy.

Problem 3

A **conditional statement** is a statement that can be written in the form "If p, then q." The portion of the statement represented by p is the **hypothesis**. The portion of the statement represented by q is the **conclusion**.

For example, in the conditional statement "If a credit card has no annual fee and a low interest rate, then Samantha will consider applying for it," the hypothesis is "A credit card has no annual fee and a low interest rate" and the conclusion is "Samantha will consider applying for it."

1. The first statement of each question in Problems 1 and 2 is a conditional statement. For each, underline the hypothesis with a solid line. Then underline the conclusion with a dashed line.

   One way to prove the statement "If p, then q" is by using the argument "If not q, then not p." Another way to say this is "If q is false, then p is false." This type of argument is called **proof by contrapositive**.

2. Which conclusions in Problems 1 and 2 used proof by contrapositive? Print the word *contrapositive* beside each conclusion that used proof by contrapositive.

The remaining questions in Problems 1 and 2 use a form of proof called a **direct argument**. Each direct argument includes a conditional statement, a second statement formed by the hypothesis of the conditional statement, and a conclusion formed by the conclusion of the conditional statement.

Problem 4

A friend asks you to check her homework. One problem required her to simplify the expression $(x + y)^2$. She wrote $(x + y)^2 = x^2 + y^2$.

Your friend's work is a conditional statement even though it is not written in the form "If p, then q." However, it can be rewritten as "If x and y are numbers, then $(x + y)^2 = x^2 + y^2$."

1. Prove whether the conditional statement is true or false.

    a. Choose two numbers for x and y, neither of which is 0.

    b. Substitute your values for x and y into both sides of the equation. Then simplify each side of the equation.

    c. Is your friend's conditional statement true for all numbers? Explain.

A specific example that shows that a conditional statement is false is called a **counterexample**. Using a counterexample is a form of proof called an **indirect argument**.

2. How many counterexamples does it take to show that a conditional statement is false?

3. Is the statement "$a(b + c) = (a + b)c$ for all values of a, b, and c" true or false? If it is false, provide a counterexample.

4. Ardella notices that 3, 5, and 7 are all odd numbers and also all prime numbers. She proposes that all odd numbers are prime numbers.

a. Did Ardella use inductive or deductive reasoning? Explain.

b. Is Ardella correct? If she is incorrect, provide a counterexample.

Problem 5

1. What are two ways that deductive reasoning can result in a false conclusion?

2. What is the minimum that you need to do to prove that an assertion is false?

3. What kind of logical reasoning does not try to guarantee that its conclusion is true?

4. Write a false assertion. Then provide a counterexample to prove that it is false.

5. Write a conditional statement and underline the hypothesis with a solid line and the conclusion with a dashed line.

3

6. Write a direct argument using your conditional statement in Question 5. Remember that a direct argument includes a conditional statement, a second statement formed by the hypothesis of the conditional statement, and a conclusion formed by the conclusion of the conditional statement.

7. Write an indirect argument using your conditional statement in Question 5. Remember that an indirect argument uses the conditional statement, a second statement formed by the negation of the conclusion, and a conclusion formed by the negation of the hypothesis.

Be prepared to share your solutions and methods.

3

3.3 You Can't Handle the Truth (Table)

Converses, Inverses, Contrapositives, Biconditionals, Truth Tables, Postulates, and Theorems

Objectives

In this lesson you will:

- Explore the truth value of conditional statements.
- Use a truth table.
- Write the converse of a conditional statement.
- Write the inverse of a conditional statement.
- Write the contrapositive of a conditional statement.
- Write a biconditional statement.
- Differentiate between postulates and theorems.

Key Terms

- propositional form
- propositional variables
- truth value
- truth table
- converse
- inverse
- contrapositive
- logically equivalent
- biconditional statement
- postulate
- theorem

3

Previously, you learned that a conditional statement is a statement that can be written in the form "if p, then q." This form of a conditional statement is called the **propositional form.** The variable p represents the hypothesis and the variable q represents the conclusion. The variables p and q are **propositional variables.** The **truth value** of a conditional statement is whether the statement is true or false. If a conditional statement could be true, then its truth value is considered "true."

Problem 1   Truth Tables

Consider the following direct argument.

Statement: If I am 18 years old, then I can vote.

Statement: I am 18 years old.

Conclusion: Therefore, I can vote.

1. What is the conditional statement?

2. What is the hypothesis, p? Underline the hypothesis with a solid line.

3. What is the conclusion, q? Underline the conclusion with a dashed line.

4. If p is true and q is true, then the truth value of a conditional statement is "true." Use these truth values to explain why the conditional statement is always true.

5. If p is true and q is false, then the truth value of a conditional statement is "false." Use these truth values to explain why the conditional statement is always false.

6. If p is false and q is true, then the truth value of a conditional statement is "true." Use these truth values to explain why the conditional statement could be true.

7. If p is false and q is false, then the truth value of a conditional statement is "true." Use these truth values to explain why the conditional statement could be true.

Questions 4 through 7 can be summarized using a **truth table** for p and q as shown. The first two columns of the truth table represent the possible truth values for p and q. The last column represents the truth value of the conditional statement ($p \mapsto q$). Notice that the truth value of a conditional statement is either "true" or "false," but not both.

p	q	$p \rightarrow q$
T	T	T
T	F	F
F	T	T
F	F	T

8. Consider the conditional statement "If an animal is a lion, then the animal is a mammal."

a. What is the hypothesis, p?

b. What is the conclusion, q?

c. Assume that p is true and q is true. What does that mean?

d. Could this statement be true? What is the truth value of the conditional statement when p is true and q is true?

e. Assume that p is true and q is false. What does that mean?

f. Could this statement be true? What is the truth value of the conditional statement when p is true and q is false?

g. Assume that p is false and q is true. What does that mean?

h. Could this statement be true? What is the truth value of the conditional statement when p is false and q is true?

i. Assume that p is false and q is false. What does that mean?

j. Could this statement be true? What is the truth value of the conditional statement when p is false and q is false?

Problem 2 Converses

The **converse** of a conditional statement of the form "If p, then q" is the statement of the form "If q, then p." The converse is a new statement that results when the hypothesis and conclusion of the conditional statement are switched.

For each conditional statement written in propositional form, identify the hypothesis, p, and conclusion, q. Then write the converse of the conditional statement.

1. If a quadrilateral is a square, then the quadrilateral is a rectangle.

    a. Hypothesis, p:

    b. Conclusion, q:

    c. Is the conditional statement true? Explain.

    d. Converse:

    e. Is the converse true? Explain.

2. If an integer is even, then the integer is divisible by two.

   a. Hypothesis, *p*:

   b. Conclusion, *q*:

   c. Is the conditional statement true? Explain.

   d. Converse:

   e. Is the converse true? Explain.

3. If a polygon has six sides, then the polygon is a pentagon.

   a. Hypothesis, *p*:

   b. Conclusion, *q*:

   c. Is the conditional statement true? Explain.

   d. Converse:

   e. Is the converse true? Explain.

4. If two lines intersect, then the lines are perpendicular.

   a. Hypothesis, *p*:

   b. Conclusion, *q*:

   c. Is the conditional statement true? Explain.

   d. Converse:

   e. Is the converse true? Explain.

5. What do you notice about the truth value of a conditional statement and the truth value of its converse?

Problem 3   Inverses

The **inverse** of a conditional statement of the form "If p, then q" is the statement of the form "If not p, then not q." The inverse is a new statement that results when the hypothesis and conclusion of the conditional statement are negated.

For each conditional statement written in propositional form, identify the hypothesis p and conclusion q. Then identify the negation of the hypothesis and conclusion and write the inverse of the conditional statement.

1. If a quadrilateral is a square, then the quadrilateral is a rectangle.

   a. Hypothesis, p:

   b. Conclusion, q:

   c. Is the conditional statement true? Explain.

   d. Not p:

   e. Not q:

   f. Inverse:

   g. Is the inverse true? Explain.

2. If an integer is even, then the integer is divisible by two.

   a. Hypothesis, p:

   b. Conclusion, q:

   c. Is the conditional statement true? Explain.

d. Not *p*:

e. Not *q*:

f. Inverse:

g. Is the inverse true? Explain.

3. If a polygon has six sides, then the polygon is a pentagon.

   a. Hypothesis, *p*:

   b. Conclusion, *q*:

   c. Is the conditional statement true? Explain.

   d. Not *p*:

   e. Not *q*:

   f. Inverse:

   g. Is the inverse true? Explain.

4. If two lines intersect, then the lines are perpendicular.

   a. Hypothesis, *p*:

   b. Conclusion, *q*:

   c. Is the conditional statement true? Explain.

   d. Not *p*:

   e. Not *q*:

   f. Inverse:

   g. Is the inverse true? Explain.

5. What do you notice about the truth value of a conditional statement and the truth value of its inverse?

Problem 4   Contrapositives

The **contrapositive** of a conditional statement of the form "if p, then q" is the statement of the form "if not q, then not p." The contrapositive is a new statement that results when the hypothesis and conclusion of the conditional statement are negated and switched.

For each conditional statement written in propositional form, identify the negation of the hypothesis and conclusion and write the contrapositive of the conditional statement.

1. If a quadrilateral is a square, then the quadrilateral is a rectangle.

    a. Is the conditional statement true? Explain.

    b. Not p:

    c. Not q:

    d. Contrapositive:

    e. Is the contrapositive true? Explain.

2. If an integer is even, then the integer is divisible by two.

    a. Is the conditional statement true? Explain.

    b. Not p:

    c. Not q:

    d. Contrapositive:

    e. Is the contrapositive true? Explain.

3. If a polygon has six sides, then the polygon is a pentagon.

    a. Is the conditional statement true? Explain.

    b. Not p:

    c. Not q:

    d. Contrapositive:

    e. Is the contrapositive true? Explain.

4. If two lines intersect, then the lines are perpendicular.

    a. Is the conditional statement true? Explain.

    b. Not p:

    c. Not q:

    d. Contrapositive:

    e. Is the contrapositive true? Explain.

5. What do you notice about the truth value of a conditional statement and the truth value of its contrapositive?

Problem 5

1. Do you agree or disagree with each statement? If you disagree, provide a counterexample.

   a. If a conditional statement is true, then its converse is true.

   b. If a conditional statement is true, then its inverse is true.

   c. If a conditional statement is true, then its contrapositive is true.

Two propositional forms are **logically equivalent** if they have the same truth values for corresponding values of the propositional variables.

2. Look at the four conditional statements used in Problems 2 through 4. Which conditional statement contained the most examples of logically equivalent relationships?

Problem 6

The negation of a statement, *p*, is logically equivalent to the statement "It is not true that *p*." The negation of a statement, *p*, is represented as "not *p*" or ~*p*.

1. If the truth value of *p* is "true," what is the truth value of ~*p*?

2. If the truth value of *p* is "false," what is the truth value of ~*p*?

3. Complete the following truth table.

				Conditional	
p	~*p*	*q*	~*q*	*p* → ~*q*	~*q* → ~*p*
T		T			
T		F			
F		T			
F		F			

4. What do you notice about the last two columns?

5. The truth table proves that a conditional statement is logically equivalent to what other propositional form?

Problem 7 Biconditional Statements

When a conditional statement and its converse are both true, they can be combined and written as a single statement using "if and only if." This new statement is called a **biconditional statement**.

For example:

Conditional Statement: If a quadrilateral has four right angles, then the quadrilateral is a rectangle.

Converse: If a quadrilateral is a rectangle, then the quadrilateral has four right angles.

The conditional statement and its converse are both true. So, they can be rewritten as a biconditional statement.

Biconditional: A quadrilateral has four right angles if and only if the quadrilateral is a rectangle.

For each conditional statement, write the converse. If possible, write a true biconditional statement. If it is not possible, explain why.

1. If a triangle has at least two congruent sides, then the triangle is isosceles.

   a. Converse:

   b. Biconditional:

2. If two lines are parallel, then the two lines do not intersect.

   a. Converse:

   b. Biconditional:

3. If two circles have equal length radii, then the two circles are congruent.

   a. Converse:

   b. Biconditional:

4. If a quadrilateral is a square, then the quadrilateral is a rectangle.

   a. Converse:

   b. Biconditional:

5. If an angle is bisected, then the angle is divided into two angles of equal measure.

   a. Converse:

   b. Biconditional:

3

Problem 8   Postulates and Theorems

A **postulate** is a statement that is accepted without proof. A **theorem** is a statement that can be proven.

The Elements is a book written by the Ancient Greek mathematician Euclid. He used a small number of postulates to systematically prove many theorems.

Consider Euclid's first three postulates.

- Line Postulate: Exactly one line can be constructed through any two points.

- Line Intersection Postulate: The intersection of two lines is exactly one point.

- Midpoint Postulate: Exactly one midpoint can be constructed in any line segment.

One theorem that Euclid was able to prove is the Pythagorean Theorem, which summarizes the relationship between the three sides of a right triangle. One proof uses the area of squares. Use the graph below to explore proving the Pythagorean Theorem.

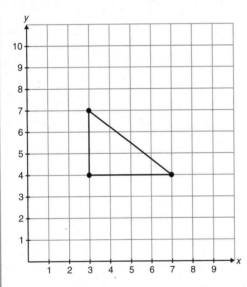

1. Construct three squares, each sharing one side of the right triangle.

2. What do you need to know to calculate the area of each square?

3. The length of the horizontal side of the triangle is 4 units. The length of the vertical side of the triangle is 3 units. The length of the longest side of the triangle is 5 units. What is the area of each square?

4. How does the sum of the areas of the small and medium squares compare to the area of the large square?

5. Consider a triangle with side lengths of 6 units, 8 units, and 10 units. What is the area of each square?

6. How does the sum of the areas of the small and medium squares compare to the area of the large square?

7. Consider a right triangle with side lengths of *a* units, *b* units, and *c* units. What is the area of each square?

8. How does the sum of the areas of the small and medium squares compare to the area of the large square?

9. State the Pythagorean Theorem.

10. How many sets of numbers would you need to test to prove this theorem? Explain. Is this possible?

11. How can you prove that a theorem is true for all numbers?

 Be prepared to share your solutions and methods.

3

3.4 Proofs Aren't Just for Geometry

Introduction to Direct and Indirect Proof with the Properties of Numbers

Objectives

In this lesson you will:

- Use the commutative, associative, identity, and inverse laws for addition and multiplication.
- Use the distributive law.
- Use direct proof to prove a theorem.
- Use indirect proof to prove a theorem.

Key Terms

- commutative law
- associative law
- identity law
- inverse law
- distributive law
- proof by contradiction

Problem 1   Direct Proofs and Number Laws

3

1. Some conditional statements can be proven using a direct proof. Read the conditional statement and each step of the direct proof. For each step, explain what changed from the previous step.

Conditional Statement: If $a + bc = c(b + a) + a$, then $a = 0$ or $c = 0$

Steps	What Changed?
$a + bc = cb + ca + a$	
$a + bc = bc + ca + a$	
$a + bc = ca + a + bc$	
$a + bc - bc = ca + a + bc - bc$	
$a = ca + a$	
$a - a = ca + a - a$	
$0 = ca$	
$a = 0$ or $c = 0$	

© 2009 Carnegie Learning, Inc.

Complete the table to summarize the real number laws. The following laws are true for any real numbers a, b, and c.

2.

Name of Law	Symbolic Representation of Law Under Addition	Symbolic Representation of Law Under Multiplication
Commutative	$a + b = b + a$	
Associative		$a(bc) = (ab)c$
Identity	$a + 0 = a$	$a \cdot 1 = a$
Inverse		$a \cdot \frac{1}{a} = 1 \ (a \neq 0)$
Distributive	$a(b + c) = ab + ac$	

3. Complete the direct proof from Question 1. Use the names of the laws from the table. If you cannot find a law that is a good fit, write a statement that summarizes the rule or property of real numbers.

Conditional Statement: If $a + bc = c(b + a) + a$, then $a = 0$ or $c = 0$

Steps   **Reasons**

$a + bc = cb + ca + a$

$a + bc = bc + ca + a$

$a + bc = ca + a + bc$

$a + bc - bc$
     $= ca + a + bc - bc$

$a = ca + a$

$a - a = ca + a - a$

$0 = ca$

$a = 0$ or $c = 0$

Consider the associative laws $(a + b) + c = a + (b + c)$, and $a(bc) = (ab)c$.

The associative law can be stated in words as:

> *When three terms are added, the first two terms can be grouped or the last two terms can be grouped.*

> *When three factors are multiplied, the first two factors can be grouped or the last two factors can be grouped.*

4. State the commutative law in words.

5. State the identity law in words.

6. State the inverse law in words.

7. State the distributive law in words.

Problem 2   Indirect Proofs

In Problem 1, you used a direct proof to prove the theorem "If $a + bc = c(b + a) + a$, then $a = 0$ or $c = 0$." This theorem can also be proven using an indirect proof called **proof by contradiction**.

To prove a statement using proof by contradiction, assume that the conclusion is false. Then show that the hypothesis is false or a contradiction. This is equivalent to showing that if the hypothesis is true, then the conclusion is also true.

Begin by assuming that $a \neq 0$ and $c \neq 0$. So, let $a = 2$ and $c = 2$. Substitute these values into the equation and simplify.

Complete the indirect proof. Use the names of the real number laws.

Steps	Reasons
$2 + 2b = 2(b + 2) + 2$	Assumption (negation of the conclusion)
$2 + 2b = 2b + 4 + 2$	
$2 + 2b = 4 + 2 + 2b$	
$0 = 4$	

This is a contradiction because $0 \neq 4$. So, the theorem must be true.

Problem 3   Indirect Proofs

1. Examine Kate's solution to a math problem.

   $\dfrac{ab + c}{a} = b + c$ for all real numbers a, b, and c

   a. Is Kate's solution correct?

   b. Prove your answer to part (a).

2. Prove or disprove the statement $\dfrac{ab + ac}{a} = b + c$.

3. Identify the error in the following proof.

If $a = 0$, then $5 = 7$.

1. $0 = 0$	All numbers equal themselves.
2. $5 \cdot 0 = 7 \cdot 0$	Zero times any number is equal to zero.
3. $5a = 7a$	Let $a = 0$.
4. $5a + ax = 7a + ax$	Algebraic equations remain true if you perform the same operation on both sides.
5. $a(5 + x) = a(7 + x)$	Distributive law of multiplication with respect to addition.
6. $\dfrac{a(5 + x)}{a} = \dfrac{a(7 + x)}{a}$	Algebraic equations remain true if you perform the same operation on both sides.
7. $5 + x = 7 + x$	Inverse law of multiplication
8. $5 = 7$	Algebraic equations remain true if you perform the same operation on both sides.

Problem 4

Complete the table to summarize the real number laws. The following laws are true for any real numbers a, b, and c.

Don't look back!

Name of Law	Symbolic Representation of Law Under Addition	Symbolic Representation of Law Under Multiplication

Be prepared to share your solutions and methods.

4 Modeling with Functions

Tiles were first used to make roofs in ancient Greece, where they were popular for their fire-resistant properties. Modern tiles are used in many building and decorative applications. You will learn how to use geometric patterns, numeric patterns, and algebraic functions to calculate the number of tiles needed to construct a patterned tile floor.

4

4.1 Squares and More
Using Patterns to Generate Algebraic Functions

Objectives

In this lesson you will:

- Generate algebraic functions using numeric and geometric patterns.
- Represent algebraic functions in different forms.

Problem 1

Terrance owns a flooring company. His latest job involves tiling a square room that is 101 feet by 101 feet. The customer requested a pattern of alternating black, white, and grey tiles as shown. Each tile is one square foot.

  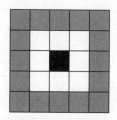

1. Sketch the design for a square floor that is 9 feet by 9 feet.

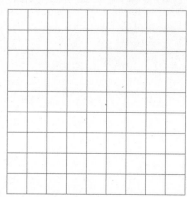

2. Complete the following table to summarize the number and color of tiles used.

Tiles Along Edge of Floor	1	3	5	7	9
Black tiles	1	1	1		
White tiles	0	8	8		
Grey tiles	0	0	16		
New tiles	1	8	16		
Total tiles	1	9	25		

3. How many times will Terrance need to repeat this pattern to complete the room?

4. Continue the table:

Tiles Along Edge of Floor	11	13	15
Black tiles			
White tiles			
Grey tiles			
New tiles			
Total tiles			

5. Why is the number of tiles along the edge of the floor increasing by 2 each time?

6. How many total tiles will Terrance need to cover the entire room? Explain.

Terrance needs to know how many tiles are required to complete the job. He asks several co-workers how many new tiles must be added to a square with side length n tiles to build the next square. Each begins by explaining how many tiles should be added to a square with a side length of 3 tiles. Then each generalizes.

7. Wilma says that you must add 3 tiles to each of the four sides of the white square, which is 4 · 3 tiles. Then you must add 1 tile at each corner. So, the number of additional tiles added to a 3 × 3 square is 4 · 3 + 4. Using Wilma's pattern, write an expression for the number of tiles that must be added to an n × n square.

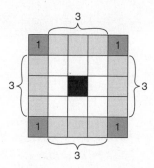

8. Howard says that you must add 5 tiles to two of the sides and 3 tiles to the other two sides. So, the number of additional tiles added to a 3 × 3 square is 2(3 + 2) + 2 · 3. Using Howard's pattern, write an expression for the number of tiles that must be added to an n × n square.

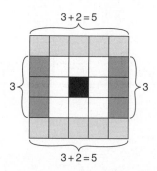

9. Kenesha says that you really have two squares. The original square has 3 · 3 tiles. The newly formed square has 5 · 5 tiles. So, the number of additional tiles added to a 3 × 3 square is 5 · 5 − 3 · 3. Using Kenesha's pattern, write an expression for the number of tiles that must be added to an n × n square.

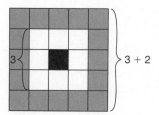

4

10. Finally, Lebron says that you need to add 3 tiles four times and then add the four corners. So, the number of additional tiles added to a 3 × 3 square is $3 + 3 + 3 + 3 + 4$. Using Lebron's pattern, write an expression for the number of tiles that must be added to an $n \times n$ square.

11. Use the expressions from Questions 7–10 to calculate the number of tiles that must be added to squares with side lengths of 11 tiles and 13 tiles.

a. Wilma's formula:

b. Howard's formula:

c. Kenesha's formula:

d. Lebron's formula:

12. Whose expression is correct? Explain.

13. Show why the expressions are equivalent.

Problem 2

Now that Terrance knows how many tiles must be added to each square, he wants to create stacks of tiles so that the tiles for each new row added to the black center tile are stacked together. First, Terrance must know the color of the tiles in each stack.

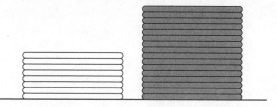

1. Complete the table.

Stack Number	1	2	3	4	5
Color	white	grey			

2. List the stack numbers that contain white tiles.

3. The white stack numbers can be represented by an arithmetic sequence. Write an explicit formula to represent a general term, a_w, of this sequence.

4. List the stack numbers that contain grey tiles.

5. The grey stack numbers can be represented by an arithmetic sequence. Write an explicit formula to represent a general term, a_g, of this sequence.

6. List the stack numbers that contain black tiles.

7. The black stack numbers can be represented by an arithmetic sequence. Write an explicit formula to represent a general term, a_b, of this sequence.

8. Use the explicit formulas to determine the color of the tiles in each stack.

   a. 33rd stack:

   b. 41st stack:

   c. 28th stack:

Problem 3

Finally, Terrance must know the number of tiles in each stack.

1. Complete the table.

Stack Number	1	2	3	4	5	n
Tiles Along Edge of Floor	3	5	7			
Number of Tiles in Stack	8	16				

2. Write an expression for the number of tiles along the edge of the floor for the nth stack.

3. How many stacks are required to complete the job? Explain.

4. Write an expression for the number of tiles in the nth stack.

5. How many tiles are in the last stack? Explain.

6. For each stack, determine the number of tiles in the stack and the side length of the square that is created using that stack.

a. Stack 26:

b. Stack 43:

c. Stack 36:

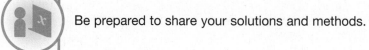
Be prepared to share your solutions and methods.

4

Objectives

In this lesson you will:

- Represent functions using words, tables, equations, graphs, and diagrams.
- Analyze functions using multiple representations.

Problem 1

A company owns a large plot of land. They want to divide the large plot into smaller plots consisting of square lots, *x* feet on a side, with a 10-foot-wide driveway along one side as shown.

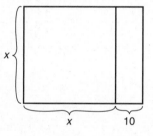

1. What is the area of each square lot? Label the diagram.

2. What is the area of each driveway? Label the diagram.

3. Use area composition to write an expression for the area of the square lot and the driveway.

4. What is the length of the square lot and the driveway?

5. What is the width of the square lot and the driveway?

6. Use the length and width from Questions 4 and 5 to write an expression for the area of the square lot and the driveway.

7. You wrote the total area in two different ways in Questions 3 and 6. Show how these expressions are equivalent.

8. Complete the table.

Width of Square Lot	Length of Plot	Area of Square Lot	Area of Driveway	Total Area of Plot
10	20	100	100	200
30				
50				
100				
x				

9. Write a function $A(x)$ to represent the total area of the lot and the driveway for a lot with side length x.

10. What are the domain and range of $A(x)$ in terms of the problem situation?

11. Graph $A(x)$.

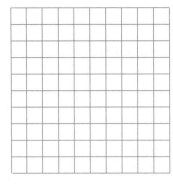

12. List the different ways that the problem situation was represented.

Problem 2

A second developer is dividing a similar plot of land into smaller plots consisting of square lots, x feet on a side, with a 10-foot-wide driveway along one side and a 3-foot-wide walkway along another side as shown.

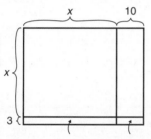

1. What is the area of each square lot? Label the diagram.

2. What is the area of each driveway? Label the diagram.

3. What is the area of each walkway adjacent to the square lot? Label the diagram.

4. What is the area of each walkway adjacent to the driveway? Label the diagram.

4

5. Use area composition to write an expression for the total area of the square lot, the driveway, and the walkway.

6. What is the length of the square lot, driveway, and walkway?

7. What is the width of the square lot, driveway, and walkway?

8. Use the length and width from Questions 6 and 7 to write an expression for the total area of the square lot, the driveway, and the walkway.

9. You wrote the total area in two different ways in Questions 5 and 8. Show how these expressions are equivalent.

10. Complete the table.

Width of Square Lot	Width of Plot	Length of Plot	Area of Square Lot	Area of Walkway	Area of Driveway	Total Area
10	13	20	100	60	100	260
30						
50						
100						
x						

11. Write a function $A(x)$ to represent the total area of the lot, driveway, and walkway for a lot with side length x.

12. What are the domain and range of $A(x)$ in terms of the problem situation?

4

13. Graph $A(x)$.

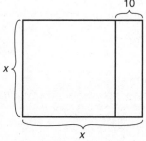

Problem 3

A third developer is dividing a similar plot of land into smaller plots consisting of square lots, x feet on a side, with a 10-foot-wide driveway within the square lot as shown.

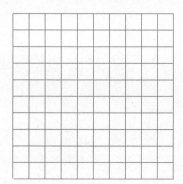

1. What is the area of each square lot? Label the diagram.

2. What is the area of each driveway? Label the diagram.

3. Use area composition to write an expression for the area of the plot not covered by the driveway. Label the diagram.

4. What is the length of the plot not covered by the driveway?

5. What is the width of the plot not covered by the driveway?

6. Use the length and width from Questions 4 and 5 to write an expression for the area of the plot not covered by the driveway.

7. You wrote the total area in two different ways in Questions 3 and 6. Show how these expressions are equivalent.

8. Complete the table.

Width of Square Lot	Length of Plot Not Covered by the Driveway	Area of Square Lot	Area of Driveway	Area of Plot Not Covered by the Driveway
20	10	400	200	200
30				
50				
100				
x				

9. Write a function $A(x)$ to represent the area of the plot not covered by the driveway for a lot with side length x.

10. What are the domain and range of $A(x)$ in terms of the problem situation?

11. Graph $A(x)$.

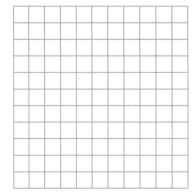

 Be prepared to share your solutions and methods.

Objective

In this lesson you will:

- Use area models to add, subtract, and multiply polynomials.

Key Terms

- polynomial
- monomial
- binomial
- trinomial

Problem 1

A **polynomial** is an expression formed by adding and subtracting terms of the form ax^n, where a is any number and n is a whole number. For example, the expressions $2x$, $x^2 + 2x + 5$, and $3x^4 - x^2 + 1$ are polynomials.

Some polynomials have special names based on the number of terms as shown in the table.

Polynomial Name	Number of Terms	Examples
monomial	one (mono)	$2x$, 5, $4x^3$
binomial	two (bi)	$x - 5$, $4x^3 + 2x$
trinomial	three (tri)	$4x^3 + x - 5$, $2x^2 + 7x - 3$

In the last lesson, you used area models to represent polynomials such as $x^2 + 3x + 10x + 30$, and $x^2 - 10x$.

1. For each sum or difference, sketch the resulting model. Then calculate the sum or difference.

   a. $(2x + 5) + (4x + 4) =$

Take Note

To distribute the negative sign:

$(4x + 2) = -(4x) - (2) = -4x - 2$

b. $(5x + 6) - (4x + 2) =$

c. $(3x^2 + 5) - (x^2 + 2) =$

d. $(x^2 + 5x) + (x^2 + 4x + 4) =$

2. Based on your results from Question 1, what must be true to add or subtract two terms?

3. Calculate each sum or difference without sketching a model.

    a. $(7x + 4) + (3x + 1) =$

    b. $(3x + 8) - (3x + 2) =$

    c. $(x^2 + 2x) + (7x + 1) =$

    d. $(2x^2 + 4x) - (x^2 + 3x) =$

    e. $(5x + 3) - (2x + 1) =$

Problem 2

A developer is dividing a plot of land into smaller plots consisting of square lots, *x* feet on each side, with a 10-foot-wide driveway within one side and a 3-foot walkway within another side as shown. The remaining portion of the lot will be used to build a home.

1. Label the dimensions on the diagram of this plot.

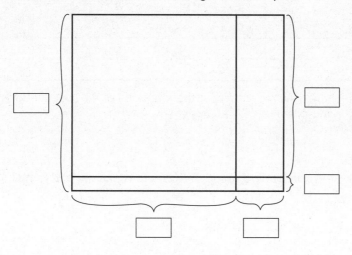

2. What is the area of each square lot?

3. What is the area of each driveway?

4. What is the area of each walkway?

5. Use area composition to write an expression for the total area of the plot used for building a home.

6. What is the length of the plot used for building a home?

7. What is the width of the plot used for building a home?

8. Use the length and width from Questions 6 and 7 to write an expression for the total area of the plot used for building a home.

9. Complete the table.

Width of Square Lot	Width of House Plot	Length of House Plot	Area of Square Lot	Area of Driveway	Area of Walkway	Area of House Plot
50	40	47	2500	470	150	1880
x						

10. Write a function $A(x)$ to represent the total area of the plot used for building a home for a lot with side length x.

11. What are the domain and range of $A(x)$ in terms of the problem situation?

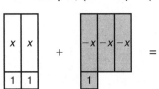

Problem 3

Using an area model for multiplying two polynomials involving subtraction is more difficult than multiplying two polynomials involving only addition. We will use a different shade to represent negative areas.

For example, $(2x + 2) + (-3x - 1) = 2x + 2 - 3x - 1 = -x + 1$.

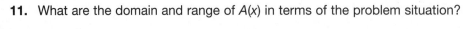

1. For each sum or difference, sketch the resulting model. Then calculate the sum or difference.

a. $(3x - 5) + (2x + 3) =$

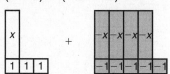

b. $(x + 3) + (-4x - 5) =$

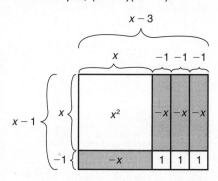

Using a different shade to represent negative areas can also be used when multiplying polynomials.

For example, $(x - 1)(x - 3) = x^2 - x - x - x - x + 1 + 1 + 1 = x^2 - 4x + 3$.

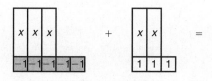

2. For each product, sketch the resulting model. Then calculate the product.

a. $(x + 2)(x + 3) =$

b. $(x + 3)(x - 5) =$

c. $(x - 2)(x - 4) =$

d. $(x - 2)(x + 2) =$

Be prepared to share your solutions and methods.

4.4 Another Factor
Dividing and Factoring Quadratic Trinomials

Objectives

In this lesson you will:

- Multiply polynomials using area models, multiplication tables, and the distributive property.
- Divide polynomials using area models, multiplication tables, and long division.
- Factor quadratic trinomials using area models.

Key Terms

- quadratic trinomial
- factoring

Problem 1   Models for Multiplication

Previously, you learned how to multiply polynomials using an area model. An area model can be used to multiply $(x + 4)(x - 5)$ as follows.

$(x + 4)(x - 5) = x^2 + 4x - 5x - 20 = x^2 - x - 20$

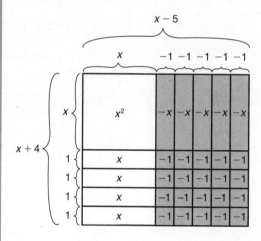

A multiplication table is a model for multiplying polynomials that is similar to an area model. A multiplication table can be used to multiply $(x + 4)(x - 5)$ as follows.

$(x + 4)(x - 5)$

·	x	4
x	x^2	$4x$
-5	$-5x$	-20

$(x + 4)(x - 5) = x^2 + 4x - 5x - 20 = x^2 - x - 20$

An area model and a multiplication table are visual representations of the distributive property. The distributive property can be used to multiply $(x + 4)(x - 5)$ as follows.

$(x + 4)(x - 5) = $ Distribute $(x + 4)$

         $= $ Distribute x and -5

         $= $

         $= $

1. Perform each multiplication using the method specified.

   a. Use an area model to multiply $(x - 3)(x - 2)$.

   b. Use the distributive property to multiply $(x + 8)(x - 7)$.

   c. Use a multiplication table to multiply $(x + 5)(x - 10)$.

2. Perform each multiplication using any method.

    a. $(x - 7)(x - 9) =$

    b. $(x + 1)(x - 1) =$

    c. $(x + 12)(x + 12) =$

    d. $(x - 7)(x - 7) =$

    e. $(x - 6)(x + 6) =$

    f. $(x - 11)(x + 20) =$

In Questions 1 and 2, you multiplied two binomials. Each product was a trinomial with an x^2 term. A trinomial that has an exponent of 2 as the largest power in any term is called a **quadratic trinomial**.

Problem 2   Dividing Polynomials with an Area Model

Some quadratic trinomials can be written as the product of two binomials. It may be useful to write a trinomial as a product to solve some problems. If one binomial is known, then you can use several methods to calculate the other binomial.

An area model can be used to divide $(x^2 + 5x + 6) \div (x + 2)$ as follows.

First, represent each part of the trinomial as a piece of the area model. In this problem, $x^2 + 5x + 6$ consists of 1 x^2 term, 5 x terms, and 6 constant terms.

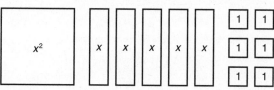

Second, use the pieces to form a rectangle with one side length equal to the known binomial. In this problem, form a rectangle with a side length of $x + 2$.

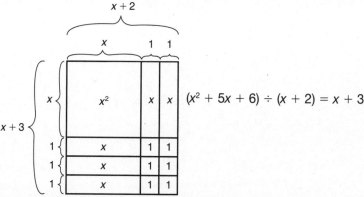

$(x^2 + 5x + 6) \div (x + 2) = x + 3$

The length of the other side of the rectangle is the quotient.

1. Perform each division using an area model.

   a. $(x^2 + 3x + 2) \div (x + 2) =$

   b. $(x^2 - 3x + 2) \div (x - 2) =$

   c. $(x^2 - x - 6) \div (x + 2) =$

A multiplication table can be used to divide $(x^2 - x - 12) \div (x + 3)$ as follows.

Enter the known binomial along the top row of the multiplication table. Enter the x^2 term and the constant term of the trinomial within the table. In this problem, enter the binomial $x + 3$ along the top row. Then enter the x^2 term and the constant term.

$\cdot$	x	3
	x^2	
		-12

Enter additional values one at a time. In this problem, the term x^2 is the result of multiplying x and some other quantity. The unknown quantity is x because x times x is x^2.

$\cdot$	x	3
x	x^2	
		-12

Multiply the x in the left column by 3 in the top row. Enter the product of $3x$.

$\cdot$	x	3
x	x^2	$3x$
		-12

The x term of the trinomial is $-x$, which is the result of adding $3x$ and some other quantity. The unknown quantity is $-4x$ because the sum of $-4x$ and $3x$ is $-x$.

$\cdot$	x	3
x	x^2	$3x$
	$-4x$	-12

The term $-4x$ is the result of multiplying x and some other quantity. The unknown quantity is -4 because x times -4 is $-4x$.

$\cdot$	x	3
x	x^2	$3x$
-4	$-4x$	-12

$(x^2 - x - 12) \div (x + 3) = x - 4$

The left column represents the quotient.

1. Perform each division using a multiplication table.

   a. $(x^2 + 4x - 5) \div (x - 1) =$

   b. $(x^2 - 7x + 12) \div (x - 4) =$

   c. $(x^2 + x - 20) \div (x + 5) =$

Problem 4   Dividing Polynomials using Long Division

A third method for dividing a trinomial by a binomial is long division. Long division can be used to divide $(x^2 - 5x - 14) \div (x + 2)$ as follows.

$$
\begin{array}{r}
x \\
x + 2\overline{)x^2 - 5x - 14} \\
\underline{x^2 + 2x} \\
-7x
\end{array}
$$
Divide, multiply and subtract

$$
\begin{array}{r}
x - 7 \\
x + 2\overline{)x^2 - 5x - 14} \\
\underline{x^2 + 2x} \\
-7x - 14 \\
\underline{-7x - 14} \\
0
\end{array}
$$
Bring down, divide, multiply and subtract

$(x^2 - 5x - 14) \div (x + 2) = x - 7$

1. Perform each division using long division.

   a. $(x^2 - 7x + 10) \div (x - 5) =$

   b. $(x^2 - 3x - 28) \div (x - 7) =$

2. Perform each division using any method.

   a. $(x^2 - 25) \div (x - 5) =$

   b. $(x^2 - 20x + 100) \div (x - 10) =$

   c. $(x^2 - 4x - 77) \div (x + 7) =$

Problem 5   Factoring Trinomials with an Area Model

Sometimes you may want to write a quadratic trinomial as the product of two binomials but you may not know either of the binomials. Each binomial is a factor of the trinomial. The process of writing a trinomial as the product of two binomials is called **factoring**.

An area model can be used to factor $x^2 + 7x + 6$ as follows.

First, represent each part of the trinomial as a piece of the area model. In this problem, $x^2 + 7x + 6$ consists of 1 x^2 term, 7 x terms, and 6 constant terms.

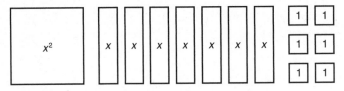

Second, use all of the pieces to form a rectangle. In this problem, the parts can only be arranged in one way.

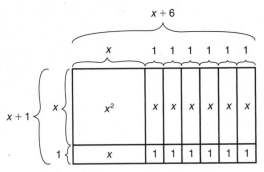

The length and width of the rectangle represents the two factors. Write the trinomial as the product of these two factors.

$x^2 + 7x + 6 =$

Factor each trinomial using an area model.

   1. $x^2 + 5x + 4 =$

2. $x^2 + 5x - 6 =$

3. $x^2 - 3x - 10 =$

4

4. $x^2 - 6x + 9 =$

Be prepared to share your solutions and methods.

4.5 More Factoring
Factoring Quadratic Trinomials

Objective

In this lesson you will:

● Factor quadratic trinomials.

Key Term

● general form of a quadratic trinomial

Problem I

An area model can be an effective tool for factoring trinomials for relatively small numbers. For example, $x^2 - 4x - 5$ requires only 12 area pieces to factor: one x^2, five $-x$'s, one x, and five -1's.

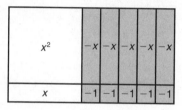

$$x^2 - 4x - 5 = (x - 5)(x + 1)$$

For trinomials with larger numbers, an area model has limited usefulness. For example, $x^2 - 10x - 24$ requires 39 area pieces to factor: one x^2, twelve $-x$'s, two x's, and twenty four -1's. For problems like this, another method is needed to factor.

The **general form of a quadratic trinomial** is $ax^2 + bx + c$, where a, b, and c are constants. In this lesson, you will be factoring quadratic trinomials where $a = 1$, which are factored as $x^2 + bx + c = (x + r_1)(x + r_2)$.

1. Look back at the quadratic trinomials that you factored using an area model. What do you notice about the constant term of the trinomial, c, and the constant of the binomial factors, r_1 and r_2?

4

2. Perform each multiplication.

    a. $(x + 1)(x + 6) =$

    b. $(x - 1)(x - 6) =$

    c. $(x + 3)(x + 2) =$

    d. $(x - 3)(x - 2) =$

    e. $(x + 1)(x - 6) =$

    f. $(x - 1)(x + 6) =$

    g. $(x - 3)(x + 2) =$

    h. $(x + 3)(x - 2) =$

3. Use the answers from Question 2 to answer each question.

    a. How are r_1 and r_2 related to c?

    b. How are r_1 and r_2 related to b?

Your answers to Question 3 point to a method for factoring any quadratic trinomial of the form $x^2 + bx + c$.

For example, to factor $x^2 - 4x - 5$ perform the following.

- List the factor pairs of the constant term c.

    In this problem the constant term is -5. Factor pairs of -5 are: -1 and 5, 1 and -5.

- Calculate the sum of each factor pair.

    $-1 + 5 = 4$

    $1 + (-5) = -4$

- Select the factor pair whose sum is equal to the coefficient of the x term, b.

- In this problem the x term is $-4x$. The coefficient of this term is -4. Select the factor pair whose sum is equal to -4. The factor pair is 1 and -5.

- Write the factors of the quadratic trinomial.

    $x^2 - 4x - 5 = (x - 5)(x + 1)$

4

4. Factor $x^2 - 10x - 24$ using this method.

    a. List the factor pairs of the constant term c.

    b. Calculate the sum of each factor pair:

    c. Select the factor pair whose sum is equal to the coefficient of the x term, b.

    d. Write the factors of the quadratic trinomial.

Problem 2

Factor each trinomial using the method from Problem 1.

    1. $x^2 - 10x + 24$

2. $x^2 + 5x - 24$

3. $x^2 - 3x - 28$

4. $x^2 - 12x - 28$

5. $x^2 - 10x + 25$

6. $x^2 - 25$

7. $x^2 - 14x + 45$

8. $x^2 - 17x + 52$

Factor each trinomial.

9. $x^2 - 16x + 15 =$

10. $x^2 - x - 12 =$

11. $x^2 + 12x + 20 =$

12. $x^2 - 49 =$

13. $x^2 - 12x + 36 =$

14. $x^2 + x - 42 =$

15. $x^2 - 16x + 48 =$

16. $x^2 - 9x + 18 =$

 Be prepared to share your solutions and methods.

4

Objectives

In this lesson you will:

- Simplify square roots.
- Multiply square roots.

Key Terms

- perfect square
- radical symbol
- radicand

Problem 1

Previously, you factored polynomials in the form $x^2 + bx + c$. For example, $x^2 - 25$ can be factored as $(x - 5)(x + 5)$.

Some polynomials, such as $x^2 - 20$, are not factorable using integers. However, they may be factorable using square roots. For example, $x^2 - 20$ can be factored using square roots as $(x - \sqrt{20})(x + \sqrt{20})$.

1. Factor each polynomial.

   a. $x^2 - 1 =$

   b. $x^2 - 100 =$

   c. $x^2 - 2 =$

   d. $x^2 - 8 =$

   e. $x^2 - 75 =$

   f. $x^2 - 144 =$

Numbers like 25 are **perfect squares**. A perfect square is a number that can be written as an integer squared. For example, 25 can be written as 5^2. The square root of a number is the number that can be multiplied by itself to result in the original number. The square root of 25 is 5 because $5^2 = 25$. The **radical symbol** $\sqrt{}$ is the mathematical symbol used to indicate a square root. The **radicand** is the expression under the radical symbol.

4

2. List the first 10 perfect squares and the square root of each.

Take Note

Pythagorean Theorem: In any right triangle, the sum of the squares of the two shorter sides, the legs, is equal to the square of the longest side, the hypotenuse.

Square roots are also useful when using the Pythagorean Theorem to calculate the third side of a right triangle.

For example, if the lengths of the legs of ΔABC are 4 feet and 6 feet, the Pythagorean Theorem can be used to calculate the length of the hypotenuse.

$$a^2 + b^2 = c^2$$

$$4^2 + 6^2 = c^2$$

$$16 + 36 = c^2$$

$$52 = c^2$$

$$\sqrt{52} = c$$

3. Calculate the missing side of each right triangle.

a. $a = 4$, $b = 7$, $c = ?$

b. $a = 6$, $b = 8$, $c = ?$

c. $a = 4$, $b = ?$, $c = 6$

d. $a = ?$, $b = 24$, $c = 25$

Problem 2

For non-zero numbers a and b, $\sqrt{a}\,\sqrt{b} = \sqrt{ab}$. For example, $\sqrt{2} \cdot \sqrt{3} = \sqrt{6}$ and $\sqrt{7} \cdot \sqrt{7} = \sqrt{49} = 7$.

1. Calculate each product.

    a. $\sqrt{4} \cdot \sqrt{4} =$

    b. $\sqrt{17} \cdot \sqrt{17} =$

    c. $\sqrt{3} \cdot \sqrt{3} =$

    d. $\sqrt{7} \cdot \sqrt{5} =$

2. Calculate each product.

    a. $\sqrt{50} \cdot \sqrt{2} =$

    b. $\sqrt{8} \cdot \sqrt{2} =$

    c. $\sqrt{32} \cdot \sqrt{2} =$

    d. $\sqrt{75} \cdot \sqrt{3} =$

To simplify a square root, write the radicand as the product of a perfect square and another factor. For example, simplify $\sqrt{12}$ as follows.

$$\sqrt{12} = \sqrt{4}\sqrt{3} = 2\sqrt{3}$$

A radical is considered completely simplified if there are no additional perfect square factors in the radicand.

3. Simplify each radical completely.

    a. $\sqrt{75} =$

    b. $\sqrt{27} =$

    c. $\sqrt{72} =$

    d. $\sqrt{48} =$

    e. $\sqrt{500} =$

    f. $\sqrt{175} =$

Take Note

You may find it easier to simplify before multiplying.

4. Calculate each product and simplify completely.

    a. $\sqrt{6}\sqrt{12} =$

    b. $\sqrt{10}\sqrt{5} =$

    c. $\sqrt{15}\sqrt{45} =$

    d. $\sqrt{50}\sqrt{14} =$

    e. $\sqrt{500}\sqrt{45} =$

    f. $\sqrt{3}(\sqrt{6} - \sqrt{15}) =$

    g. $\sqrt{12}(\sqrt{6} + \sqrt{15}) =$

    h. $\sqrt{63}\sqrt{14} =$

    i. $\sqrt{10}\sqrt{35}\sqrt{14} =$

    j. $\sqrt{33}\sqrt{44}\sqrt{15} =$

Be prepared to share your solutions and methods.

4.7 Working with Radicals
Adding, Subtracting, Dividing, and Rationalizing Radicals

Objectives

In this lesson you will:

- Add and subtract square roots.
- Divide square roots.
- Simplify square roots by rationalizing denominators.

Key Terms

- rational numbers
- irrational numbers
- rationalizing the denominator

4

Problem 1

When adding and subtracting polynomials, only terms that involve the same power, like $3x^2$ and $-5x^2$, can be added or subtracted.

When adding and subtracting square roots, only roots that have the same radicand can be added or subtracted. For example, $4\sqrt{2} + 2\sqrt{3} - \sqrt{2} = 3\sqrt{2} + 2\sqrt{3}$.

1. Calculate each sum or difference.

   a. $4\sqrt{2} + 5\sqrt{2} =$

   b. $3\sqrt{3} - 5\sqrt{3} =$

   c. $3\sqrt{3} - 5\sqrt{2} =$

   d. $7\sqrt{3} - 6\sqrt{3} - 2\sqrt{3} =$

   e. $-3\sqrt{3} - 6\sqrt{5} - 5\sqrt{5} =$

   f. $4\sqrt{2} + 2\sqrt{3} - 7\sqrt{5} =$

2. Simplify each radical. Then calculate each sum or difference.

   a. $\sqrt{8} + 5\sqrt{2} =$

   b. $\sqrt{18} - \sqrt{50} =$

   c. $2\sqrt{18} + \sqrt{12} =$

   d. $3\sqrt{28} - 5\sqrt{175} + 3\sqrt{7} =$

e. $7\sqrt{8} + 5\sqrt{32} - 3\sqrt{45} =$

f. $\sqrt{125} + 5\sqrt{7} - 3\sqrt{500} =$

Problem 2

Rational numbers are numbers that can be written in the form $\frac{a}{b}$, where a and b are integers. All integers and fractions are rational numbers. Numbers that are not rational are called **irrational numbers**. Numbers like π and square roots such as $\sqrt{2}$ are irrational numbers.

You can prove that $\sqrt{2}$ is irrational using an indirect proof.

Assume that $\sqrt{2}$ is a rational number and can be written in the form $\sqrt{2} = \frac{a}{b}$, where a and b are integers, one number odd and the other even.

1. Enter the reasons for each of the steps in the proof.

$$\sqrt{2} = \frac{a}{b}$$

$$b(\sqrt{2}) = b\left(\frac{a}{b}\right)$$

$$\sqrt{2}b = a$$

$$(\sqrt{2}b)^2 = a^2$$

$$2b^2 = a^2$$

$\therefore a^2$ must be even   Definition of even number

$\therefore a$ must be even   The square root of an even number must be even

Let $a = 2n$ Definition of even number

$$a^2 = 4n^2$$

$$2b^2 = 4n^2$$

$$b^2 = 2n^2$$

$\therefore b^2$ must be even

b must be even   The square root of an even number must be even

But this is a contradiction.

So $\sqrt{2} \neq \frac{a}{b}$ and $\sqrt{2}$ is not rational.

$\therefore \sqrt{2}$ is irrational

The decimal approximations of $\sqrt{2}$ and $\sqrt{3}$ are:

$\sqrt{2} \approx$ 1.4142135623 7309504880 1688724209 6980785696 7187537694
8073176679 7379907324 78462 ...

$\sqrt{3} \approx$ 1.7320508075 6887729352 7446341505 8723669428 0525381038
0628055806 9794519330 16909 ...

Radicals like $\sqrt{2}$ and $\sqrt{3}$ are decimals with an infinite number of decimal places. It is not possible to calculate exact results with the decimal representation. Dividing by an approximation of an irrational number often creates rounding errors. But multiplying by an approximation of an irrational number does not introduce as many rounding errors. So, it is desirable to rewrite expressions involving irrational numbers to involve multiplication instead of division.

Problem 3

Rationalizing the denominator is a process of rewriting an expression so that the denominator does not contain a radical.

To rationalize the denominator, multiply by a form of one that results in a perfect square in the radicand of the denominator. For example, to simplify $\dfrac{5}{\sqrt{2}}$, perform the following.

$$\frac{5}{\sqrt{2}} \cdot \frac{\sqrt{2}}{\sqrt{2}} = \frac{5\sqrt{2}}{\sqrt{4}} = \frac{5\sqrt{2}}{2}$$

A radical expression is not considered completely simplified if a radical exists in a denominator.

1. Simplify each expression by rationalizing the denominator.

   a. $\dfrac{4}{\sqrt{2}} =$

   b. $-\dfrac{6}{\sqrt{3}} =$

   c. $\dfrac{35}{\sqrt{14}} =$

   d. $\dfrac{2\sqrt{5}}{\sqrt{15}} =$

4

2. Simplify each expression completely.

a. $\dfrac{2\sqrt{5}}{3} + \dfrac{\sqrt{125}}{3} =$

b. $2\sqrt{7} - 2\sqrt{63} =$

c. $\dfrac{3\sqrt{5}}{4} \cdot \dfrac{2\sqrt{5}}{\sqrt{3}} =$

d. $\dfrac{3\sqrt{525}}{\sqrt{28}} =$

e. $-\dfrac{\sqrt{72}}{5\sqrt{3}} =$

f. $\dfrac{2\sqrt{5}}{7} \div \dfrac{3\sqrt{5}}{\sqrt{3}} =$

g. $\dfrac{5\sqrt{5}}{7} \cdot \dfrac{7\sqrt{15}}{2\sqrt{12}} =$

h. $\dfrac{10\sqrt{99}}{\sqrt{45}} =$

i. $\dfrac{5\sqrt{55}}{6} \cdot \dfrac{3\sqrt{75}}{2\sqrt{24}} =$

Be prepared to share your solutions and methods.

4.8   Rain Gutters
Modeling with Functions

Objectives

In this lesson you will:

- Use multiple representations of functions to model and solve problems.
- Use multiple representations of functions to analyze problems.

Problem 1

A contractor has asked you for some help. The contractor is making customized rain gutters for a house. To form the gutters, he uses long rectangular sheets of metal and bends two sides up. An end view of the gutter is shown.

Side length

Bottom width

The contractor is using metal sheets that are 8.5 inches wide. The length of each metal sheet is not important for this problem. The contractor wants to know the relationship between the side length and bottom width of each gutter. He also wants to know all of the possible side-length and bottom-width measurements that can be used to construct gutters.

1. Use sheets of paper that are 8.5 inches wide to construct 5 different gutters. Make some gutters short and wide; make others tall and narrow. In the table below, record the side-length and bottom-width measurements of each gutter you construct.

Labels	Gutter	Side Length	Bottom Width
Units		Inches	Inches
	Gutter 1		
	Gutter 2		
	Gutter 3		
	Gutter 4		
	Gutter 5		

2. Complete the table. If necessary, construct models of each gutter.

Side Length	Bottom Width
Inches	Inches
0	
0.25	
0.5	
0.75	
1	
1.25	
1.5	
1.75	
2	
2.25	
2.5	
2.75	
3	
3.25	
3.5	
3.75	
4	
4.25	

3. Based on the table, describe the relationship between the side length and bottom width.

4. As the side length increases by a quarter inch, how does the bottom width change?

5. As the side length increases by one half inch, how does the bottom width change?

6. As the side length increases by one inch, how does the bottom width change?

7. Describe how to calculate the bottom width for any side length.

8. Define a function $w(l)$ for the bottom width for a side length of l inches.

9. Graph the function $w(l)$.

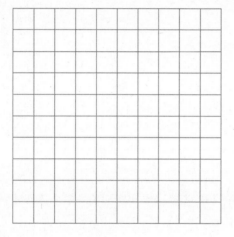

10. What are the range and domain of $w(l)$?

11. What type of function is $w(l)$?

Problem 2

The cross-sectional area of a gutter is important because a larger area can carry more rain.

Cross sectional area

Side length

Bottom width

1. Calculate the cross-sectional area for a gutter with a side length of:

   a. 2 inches.

   b. 3 inches.

   c. 2.5 inches.

2. Define a function $A(l)$ for the cross sectional area of a gutter with a side length of l inches.

3. Complete the table.

Labels	Side Length	Cross-Sectional Area
Units	**Inches**	**Square Inches**
Expression	0	
	0.5	
	1	
	1.5	
	2	
	2.5	
	3	
	3.5	
	4	

4. Graph the function $A(l)$

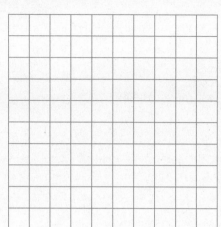

5. What type of function is $A(l)$?

6. Set the function $A(l)$ equal to 0. Calculate the values of l by factoring the equation and setting each factor to 0.

7. What are the intercepts of $A(l)$? What does each mean in terms of the problem? Label each intercept on the graph.

8. Where is the vertex? What does it mean in the problem? Label the vertex on the graph.

9. What are the domain and range of $A(l)$?

10. What is the equation of the axis of symmetry? Label the axis of symmetry on the graph.

 Be prepared to share your solutions and methods.

4.9 More Areas
More Modeling with Functions

Objectives

In this lesson you will:

- Use multiple representations of functions to model and solve problems.
- Use multiple representations of functions to analyze problems.

Problem 1

A developer is planning plots of land. Each plot consists of a square lot that is x feet on each side. A 3-foot walkway surrounds the square lot on three sides. A 10-foot driveway surrounds the square lot on the fourth side.

1. Draw a diagram of the plot that includes the square lot, walkway, and driveway. Label all dimensions in the diagram.

   What is the area of the square lot?

2. What is the area of the walkway? Write the area as a simplified expression.

3. What is the area of the driveway? Write the area as a simplified expression.

4. What is the combined area of the walkway and the driveway? Write the area as a simplified expression.

5. What is the total area of the plot? Write the area as a simplified expression.

6. What is the width of the plot?

7. What is the length of the plot?

8. Use the length and width from Questions 7 and 8 to write an expression for the area of the plot.

9. You wrote the area of the plot in two different ways in Questions 5 and 8. Show how these expressions are equivalent.

10. Write an expression for the area of the plot minus the area of the square lot. Write this area as a simplified expression.

11. What does the expression in Question 10 represent in the problem?

12. The square lot is 100 feet on each side. Calculate each area.

a. Area of the square lot

b. Area of the walkway

c. Area of the driveway

d. Area of the plot

Problem 2

A developer is planning plots of land. Each plot consists of a rectangular lot with a width of x feet and a length of $x + 6$ feet. A 3-foot walkway is adjacent to each of the shorter sides of the rectangular lot. A 10-foot driveway is adjacent to each of the longer sides of the rectangular lot. The driveways extend to the end of the walks.

1. Draw a diagram of the plot that includes the square lot, walkway, and driveway. Label all dimensions in the diagram.

2. What is the area of the rectangular lot? Write the area as a simplified expression.

3. What is the area of the walkways? Write the area as a simplified expression.

4

4. What is the area of the driveways?

5. What is the combined area of the walkway and the driveway? Write the area as a simplified expression.

6. What is the total area of the plot? Write the area as a simplified expression.

7. What is the width of the plot?

8. What is the length with the plot?

9. Use the length and width from Questions 7 and 8 to write an expression for the area of the plot.

10. You wrote the area of the plot in two different ways in Questions 6 and 9. Show how these expressions are equivalent.

11. Write an expression for the area of the plot minus the area of the rectangular lot. Write this area as a simplified expression.

12. What does the expression in Question 11 represent in the problem?

13. A rectangular lot has a width of 100 feet. Calculate each area.

   a. Area of the rectangular lot

b. Area of the walkways

c. Area of the driveways

d. Area of the plot

14. The total area of layout plot is 3120 square feet. Calculate the dimensions of the rectangular lot by performing the following steps.

   a. Set the expression for the total area of the plot equal to 3120.

   b. Transform the equation so that one side is equal to zero.

   c. Factor the expression on the other side of the equation.

   d. Set each factor equal to zero and solve.

Be prepared to share your solutions and methods.

4

5 Properties of Triangles

The largest food industry in the world is growing grapes. About 25 million acres of land are used to produce over 72 million tons of grapes each year. You will use congruent triangles to construct posts for growing grape vines.

5

5

5.1 Properties of Triangles
Angle Relationships in a Triangle

Objectives

In this lesson you will:

- Classify triangles using the measures of the interior angles.
- Determine the relationship between the measures of interior angles of a triangle and the lengths of sides of a triangle.
- Identify the remote interior angles of a triangle.
- Identify the exterior angle of a triangle.
- Solve problems using the relationship between an exterior angle of a triangle and remote interior angles.
- Prove the Exterior Angle Inequality Theorem.

Key Terms

- acute triangle
- obtuse triangle
- right triangle
- equiangular triangle
- exterior angle
- remote interior angles
- Exterior Angle Inequality Theorem

Problem 1   Classifying Triangles

One way to classify a triangle is by the measure of the interior angles. These classifications include acute triangles, obtuse triangles, and right triangles.

1. An **acute triangle** is a triangle that has three acute angles.

   a. Draw an acute triangle with three interior angles of different measure. Measure each interior angle.

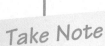

Take Note

The Triangle Sum Theorem states that the sum of the measures of the interior angles of a triangle is 180°.

   b. Measure the length of each side of the triangle.

c. The longest side of the triangle is opposite which interior angle?

d. The shortest side of the triangle is opposite which interior angle?

2. An **obtuse triangle** is a triangle that has one obtuse angle.

   a. Draw an obtuse triangle with three interior angles of different measure. Measure each interior angle.

   b. Measure the length of each side of the triangle.

   c. The longest side of the triangle is opposite which interior angle?

   d. The shortest side of the triangle is opposite which interior angle?

3. A **right triangle** is a triangle that has one right angle.

   a. Draw a right triangle with three interior angles of different measure. Measure each interior angle.

   b. Measure the length of each side of the triangle.

   c. The longest side of the triangle is opposite which interior angle?

   d. The shortest side of the triangle is opposite which interior angle?

4. An **equiangular triangle** is a triangle that has three equal angles.

   a. Draw an equiangular triangle. Measure each interior angle.

   b. Measure the length of each side of the triangle.

   c. What do you notice about the measures of the three interior angles of an equiangular triangle?

   d. What do you notice about the lengths of the three sides of an equiangular triangle?

5. Triangle ABC has interior angles measuring 57°, 62°, and 61°, respectively. Without drawing a picture, describe how to locate the longest and shortest sides of the triangle in terms of the measures of the interior angles.

6. For each triangle, list the sides from shortest to longest.

   a.

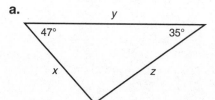

b.

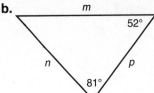

c.

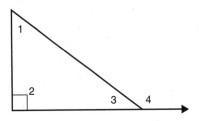

Problem 2 Exterior Angles of a Triangle

1. Use the figure shown to answer each question.

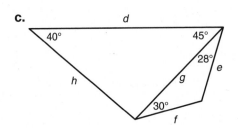

    a. Name the interior angles of the triangle.

    b. Name an **exterior angle** of the triangle.

    c. What do you need to know to answer parts a and b?

    d. What is $m\angle 1 + m\angle 2 + m\angle 3$? How do you know?

e. What is $m\angle 3 + m\angle 4$? How do you know?

f. Explain why $m\angle 1 + m\angle 2 = m\angle 4$.

2. What does the word "remote" mean in the sentence, "The treasure is buried on a remote island"?

3. Why would $\angle 1$ and $\angle 2$ be referred to as **remote interior angles** with respect to the exterior angle?

4. Write the equation $m\angle 4 = m\angle 1 + m\angle 2$ as a sentence using the words sum, remote interior angles, and exterior angle.

5. Is the equation and sentence from Question 4 a postulate or a theorem? Why?

6. Classify the triangle in Question 1 based on the angle measures.

7. Consider the relationship between the measure of an exterior angle of an acute triangle and the sum of the measures of the two remote interior angles. Is the equation from Question 4 still true? Explain.

5

8. Consider the relationship between the measure of an exterior angle of an obtuse triangle and the sum of the measures of the two remote interior angles. Is the equation from Question 4 still true? Explain.

9. You can use patty paper to explore the relationship between an exterior angle and the remote interior angles of a triangle. Perform the following steps.

Step 1: Place the patty paper over the triangle in Problem 1. Copy ∠1. Then copy ∠2 so that ∠1 and ∠2 share a common side.

Step 2: Hold the patty paper over ∠4 so that one side of ∠4 lines up with side of ∠1 and the other side of ∠4 lines up with a side of ∠2.

What do you notice?

Problem 3

Solve for *x* in each triangle.

1.

2.

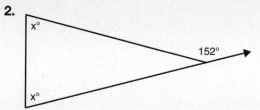

3.

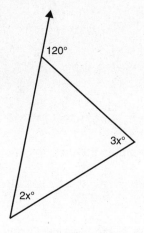

4.

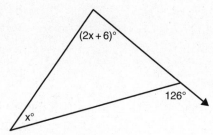

Problem 4 Exterior Angle Inequality Theorem

The **Exterior Angle Inequality Theorem** states,

The measure of an exterior angle of a triangle is greater than the measure of either of its remote interior angles.

1. Draw a triangle *ABC* with exterior angle *ACD*.

2. Use the diagram to write an inequality that states the Exterior Angle Inequality Theorem.

3. Use the diagram to explain why the Exterior Angle Inequality Theorem is true for all triangles.

4. Why is the Exterior Angle Inequality considered a theorem rather than a postulate?

Be prepared to share your solutions and methods.

Objectives

In this lesson you will:

- Classify triangles using the lengths of the sides.
- Determine the relationship between the lengths of the sides of a triangle and the measures of the interior angles of a triangle.
- Determine and apply the Triangle Inequality Theorem.

Key Terms

- scalene triangle
- isosceles triangle
- equilateral triangle

Problem 1   Classifying Triangles

One way to classify a triangle is by the lengths of the sides. These classifications include scalene triangles, isosceles triangles, and equilateral triangles.

1. A **scalene triangle** is a triangle that has three sides of different lengths.

   a. Draw a scalene triangle. Measure each side.

> **Take Note**
>
> The Triangle Sum Theorem states that the sum of the measures of the interior angles of a triangle is 180°.

   b. Measure each interior angle of the triangle.

   c. The largest interior angle of the triangle is opposite which side?

   d. The smallest interior angle of the triangle is opposite which side?

2. An **isosceles triangle** is a triangle that has two or more equal-length sides.

   a. Draw an isosceles triangle with two equal sides. Measure each side.

   b. Measure each interior angle of the triangle.

   c. The largest interior angle of the triangle is opposite which side?

   d. The smallest interior angle of the triangle is opposite which side?

3. An **equilateral triangle** is a triangle that has three equal length sides.

   a. Draw an equilateral triangle. Measure each side.

5

b. Measure each interior angle of the triangle.

c. The largest interior angle of the triangle is opposite which side?

d. The smallest interior angle of the triangle is opposite which side?

4. Triangle *ABC* has side lengths measuring 4 centimeters, 5 centimeters, and 6 centimeters, respectively. Without drawing a picture, describe how to locate the largest and smallest interior angles of the triangle in terms of the side lengths.

Problem 2

1. Sarah claims that segments of any three lengths will form a triangle. Sam believes that some combinations of segment lengths will not form a triangle. Who is correct? Explain.

2. Sam claims that he can look at the lengths of three segments and know immediately if the segments can form a triangle. Learn Sam's secret by working through the following.

Step 1: Break a piece of strand pasta at two random points. Measure the length of each pasta piece.

Step 2: Attempt to form a triangle by placing the three pieces end to end. Record your results in the first row of the following table.

Step 3: Collect the results from your classmates.

5

Piece 1 (cm)	Piece 2 (cm)	Piece 3 (cm)	Form a Triangle?

3. How many students are in your class?

4. How many students were able to form a triangle using their pasta pieces?

5. How many students were not able to form a triangle using their pasta pieces?

6. Estimate the probability that a student in your class was able to form a triangle using their pasta pieces.

7. Examine the table from Question 2. Compare the lengths that formed a triangle and the lengths that did not form a triangle.

   a. What do you notice?

   b. What must be true about the lengths for a triangle to be formed?

   c. What must be true about the lengths for a triangle to not be formed?

8. Predict whether a triangle could be formed from each set of segment lengths.

   a. 2 cm, 5.1 cm, 2.4 cm

   b. 9.2 cm, 7 cm, 1.9 cm

Problem 3

A graphing calculator can also be used to simulate the activity from Problem 2.

1. Assume that the length of a piece of pasta is 100 centimeters. Use your calculator to generate two random numbers between 0 and 100 representing the breaking points of the pasta piece. How can you calculate the length of the third pasta piece?

2. Record your results in the following table.

Trial Number	Piece 1 (cm)	Piece 2 (cm)	Piece 3 (cm)	Form a Triangle?

3. Use the table to estimate the probability that a triangle can be formed.

4. Examine your conclusion from Problem 2 Question 7. Do the calculator results agree with or contradict your original conclusion?

5. If the calculator results agree with your original conclusion, then explain why. If the calculator results contradict your original conclusion, then revise your original conclusion so that it is accurate.

6. Let's return to Sarah from Problem 2. Based on what you have learned about side lengths of triangles, state the rule Sarah must know to determine whether three segments can form a triangle.

   Be prepared to share your solutions and methods.

5

5

5.3 Properties of Triangles
Points of Concurrency

Objectives

In this lesson you will:
- Construct an angle bisector.
- Construct a perpendicular bisector.
- Construct the incenter of a triangle.
- Construct the circumcenter of a triangle.
- Construct the centroid of a triangle.
- Construct the orthocenter of a triangle.
- Compare the points of concurrency of triangles.

Key Terms
- bisect an angle
- angle bisector
- concurrent lines
- point of concurrency
- incenter
- bisect a segment
- segment bisector
- perpendicular bisector
- circumcenter
- median
- centroid
- altitude
- orthocenter

Problem 1 Constructing Angle Bisectors using a Compass and Straightedge

1. Perform the following steps using the angle shown.

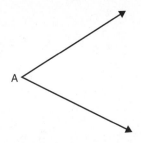

© 2009 Carnegie Learning, Inc.

a. Place the point of the compass at the vertex of the angle, point *A*. Draw an arc that intersects each side of the angle.

b. Place the point of the compass on the point where the arc intersects one side of the angle. Draw an arc in the interior of the angle.

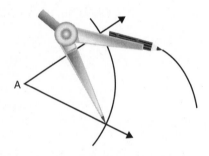

c. Place the point of the compass on the point where the arc intersects the other side of the angle. Draw an arc in the interior of the angle.

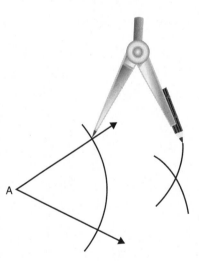

5

d. Use a straightedge to draw a line from point *A* to the intersection of the arcs from parts (b) and (c).

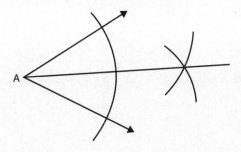

2. Use a protractor to measure the original angle from Question 1.

3. Use a protractor to measure the two angles formed from the original angle. What do you notice about the measures of these two angles and the measure of the original angle?

Question 1 asked you to **bisect an angle,** or divide the angle into two smaller angles of equal measure. An **angle bisector** is a line, segment, or ray that divides an angle into two smaller angles of equal measure.

4. An angle has a measure of 120°. What is the measure of each angle that is formed by the angle bisector? Explain.

5. An angle is bisected so that each smaller angle has a measure of 38°. What is the measure of the angle that was bisected? Explain.

Problem 2   Constructing Angle Bisectors using Patty Paper

1. Draw an angle on a piece of patty paper. Label angle *ABC*.

2. Construct the angle bisector by performing the following steps.

   a. Fold the patty paper so that *BA* and *BC* are exactly on top of each other.

   b. Unfold the patty paper and draw a ray from point *B* along the crease of the fold.

3. Use a protractor to measure the original angle from Question 1.

4. Use a protractor to measure the two angles formed from the original angle. What do you notice about the measures of these two angles and the measure of the original angle?

Problem 3   Constructing Incenters

1. Draw a right triangle. Then use a compass and straightedge to construct the angle bisector for each angle of the triangle.

2. Draw an acute triangle on patty paper. Then construct the angle bisector for each angle of the triangle.

3. Draw an obtuse triangle. Then use a compass and straightedge to construct the angle bisector for each angle of the triangle.

4. What do you notice about the angle bisectors in each triangle?

Concurrent lines are three or more lines that intersect at a common point. The point at which the lines intersect is the **point of concurrency.**

The **incenter** of a triangle is the point at which the three angle bisectors intersect.

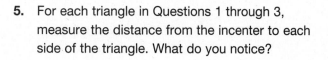

Take Note

The distance from a point to a line is the perpendicular distance from the point to the line.

5. For each triangle in Questions 1 through 3, measure the distance from the incenter to each side of the triangle. What do you notice?

5

Problem 4   Constructing Perpendicular Bisectors using a Compass and Straightedge

1. Perform the following steps using the segment shown.

A   B

a. Place the point of the compass on an endpoint of the line, point *A*. Open the compass so that it is more than half of the length of the segment. Draw an arc that intersects the line segment and extends above and below the segment.

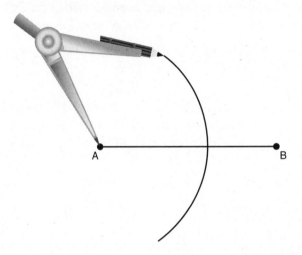

b. Keep the compass at the same width. Place the point of the compass on the other endpoint of the line, point *B*. Draw an arc that intersects the line segment and extends above and below the segment, intersecting the other arc at two points.

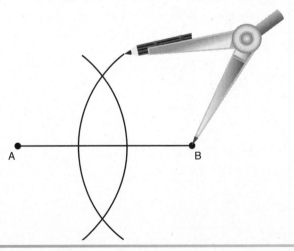

5

c. Use a straightedge to draw a line that connects the intersections of the arcs from parts (a) and (b).

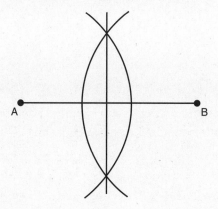

2. Use a ruler to measure the length of the original segment from Question 1.

3. Use a ruler to measure the two segments formed from the original segment. What do you notice about the lengths of these two segments and the length of the original segment?

Question 1 asked you to **bisect a segment,** or divide the segment into two smaller segments of equal length. A **segment bisector** is a line, segment, or ray that divides a segment into two smaller segments of equal length.

4. What is a name for the point on the line segment where the segment bisector intersects the line segment?

5. Use a protractor to measure each angle formed by the intersection of the segment bisector and the line segment. What do you notice?

A **perpendicular bisector** is a segment bisector that is also perpendicular to, or forms a right angle with, the line segment.

5

6. Draw a segment bisector that is not a perpendicular bisector.

7. A 24-inch line segment is bisected. What is the length of each line segment that is formed by the segment bisector? Explain.

8. A segment is bisected so that each smaller segment measures 5 millimeters. What is the length of the segment that was bisected? Explain.

Problem 5   Constructing Perpendicular Bisectors using Patty Paper

1. Draw a segment on a piece of patty paper. Label the segment *AB*.

2. Construct the perpendicular bisector by performing the following steps.

   a. Fold the patty paper so that point *A* and point *B* are exactly on top of each other.

   b. Unfold the patty paper and draw a line segment along the crease of the fold.

3. Use a ruler to measure the length of the original segment from Question 1.

4. Use a ruler to measure the length of the two segments formed from the original segment. What do you notice about the lengths of these two segments and the length of the original segment?

5. Use a protractor to measure each angle formed by the intersection of the segment bisector and the line segment. What do you notice?

Problem 6   Constructing Circumcenters

1. Draw a right triangle. Then use a compass and straightedge to construct the perpendicular bisector for each side of the triangle.

2. Draw an acute triangle on patty paper. Then construct the perpendicular bisector for each side of the triangle.

3. Draw an obtuse triangle. Then use a compass and straightedge to construct the perpendicular bisector for each side of the triangle.

4. What do you notice about the perpendicular bisectors in each triangle?

The **circumcenter** of a triangle is the point at which the three perpendicular bisectors intersect.

5. For each triangle in Questions 1 to 3, measure the distance from the circumcenter to each vertex of the triangle. What do you notice?

Problem 7 Constructing Centroids

A **median** of a triangle is a line segment that connects a vertex to the midpoint of the side opposite the vertex.

1. Which construction could you use to construct a median? Explain.

2. Draw a right triangle. Then use a compass and straightedge to construct the three medians of the triangle.

3. Draw an acute triangle on patty paper. Then construct the three medians of the triangle.

4. Draw an obtuse triangle. Then use a compass and straightedge to construct the three medians of the triangle.

5. What do you notice about the medians in each triangle?

The **centroid** of a triangle is the point at which the three medians intersect.

6. For each triangle in Questions 2 to 4, measure the distance from the vertex to the centroid. Then measure the length of the median. What do you notice?

5

Problem 8   Constructing a Perpendicular Segment from a Point not on a Line

1. Perform the following steps using the segment shown.

C

A ————————————————— B

a. Place the point of the compass on point *C*. Open the compass so that it is wide enough to cut an arc that intersects the line segment at two points. Draw this arc and label these points of intersection *D* and *E*.

b. Construct the perpendicular bisector of segment *DE*.

2. Use a protractor to measure each angle formed by the intersection of the two segments. What do you notice?

3. Use a ruler to measure the two segments formed by the original segment and the bisector. Is the line you drew the perpendicular bisector of segment *AB*? Explain.

5

Problem 9 Constructing Orthocenters

An **altitude** of a triangle is a perpendicular line segment that is drawn from a vertex to the opposite side.

1. Draw a right triangle. Then use a compass and straightedge to construct the three altitudes of the triangle.

2. Draw an acute triangle on patty paper. Then construct the three altitudes of the triangle.

3. Draw an obtuse triangle. Then use a compass and straightedge to construct the three altitudes of the triangle.

4. What do you notice about the altitudes in each triangle?

The **orthocenter** of a triangle is the point at which the three altitudes intersect.

5

Problem 10

1. Look at the constructions from Problems 2, 6, 7, and 9. Describe whether the incenter, circumcenter, centroid, and orthocenter lie in the interior, in the exterior, or on the perimeter of each type of triangle.

   a. Acute

   b. Obtuse

   c. Right

2. Can a triangle have all four points of concurrency (incenter, circumcenter, centroid, and orthocenter) as the same point? If so, draw and describe this triangle. If not, explain why.

 Be prepared to share your solutions and methods.

5.4 Properties of Triangles
Direct and Indirect Proof

Objectives

In this lesson you will:
- Prove theorems using direct proofs.
- Prove theorems using indirect proofs.

Key Terms

- Triangle Exterior Angle Theorem
- two-column proof
- negation of the conclusion
- inequality property
- Exterior Angle Inequality Theorem

Previously you learned that direct proof and indirect proof are two methods for proving theorems. In this lesson, you will prove theorems about triangles.

Problem 1

The **Triangle Exterior Angle Theorem** states:

The measure of the exterior angle of a triangle is equal to the sum of the measures of the two remote interior angles of the triangle.

In this problem, you will prove the Triangle Exterior Angle Theorem using a **two-column proof.** A two-column proof is a way of writing a proof such that each step is listed in one column and the reason for each step is listed in the other column.

1. Describe each rule, definition, postulate, or theorem.

a. Subtraction Property of Equality

b. Triangle Sum Theorem

c. Linear Pair Postulate

d. Definition of Linear Pair

2. The reasons for the proof are provided. Write each step of the proof. The final step should be what you are trying to prove.

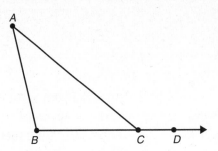

Given: Triangle *ABC* with exterior ∠*ACD*

Prove: $m\angle A + m\angle B = m\angle ACD$

Statements	Reasons
	1. Given
	2. Triangle Sum Theorem
	3. Linear Pair Postulate
	4. Definition of Linear Pair
	5. Substitution using equations from steps 2 and 4
	6. Subtraction Property of Equality

5

Problem 2

A proof by contradiction is one type of indirect proof. A proof by contradiction begins with a **negation of the conclusion,** which means that you assume the opposite of the conclusion. When a contradiction is developed, then the conclusion must be true.

1. Prove the Triangle Exterior Angle Theorem using a proof by contradiction. Each step of the proof is provided. Write a reason for each step.

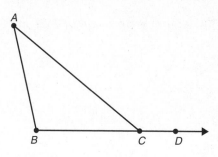

Given: Triangle ABC with exterior $\angle ACD$

Prove: $m\angle A + m\angle B = m\angle ACD$

Statements	Reasons
1. Triangle ABC with exterior $\angle ACD$	
2. $m\angle A + m\angle B \neq m\angle ACD$	
3. $m\angle A + m\angle B + m\angle BCA \neq m\angle ACD + m\angle BCA$	
4. $m\angle A + m\angle B + m\angle BCA = 180°$	
5. $\angle BCA$ and $\angle ACD$ are a linear pair	
6. $m\angle BCA + m\angle ACD = 180°$	
7. $180° \neq 180°$	

5

Problem 3

The **Exterior Angle Inequality Theorem** states:

> *An exterior angle of a triangle is greater than either of the remote interior angles of the triangle.*

The direct proof requires two parts. The first part will prove the theorem for the first remote interior angle. The second part will prove the theorem for the second remote interior angle.

1. The reasons for the first part of the proof are provided. Write each step of the proof.

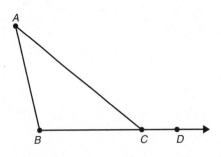

Given: Triangle *ABC* with exterior ∠*ACD*

Prove: $m\angle ACD > m\angle A$

Statements	Reasons
	1. Given
	2. Triangle Sum Theorem
	3. Linear Pair Postulate
	4. Definition of Linear Pair
	5. Substitution using equations from steps 2 and 4
	6. Subtraction Property of Equality
	7. Definition of Angle Measure
	8. Inequality Property: If $a = b + c$ and $c > 0$, then $a > b$

2. The reasons for the second part of the proof are provided. Write each step of the proof.

Given: Triangle ABC with exterior $\angle ACD$

Prove: $m\angle ACD > m\angle B$

Statements	Reasons
	1. Given
	2. Triangle Sum Theorem
	3. Linear Pair Postulate
	4. Definition of Linear Pair
	5. Substitution using equations from steps 2 and 4
	6. Subtraction Property of Equality
	7. Definition of Angle Measure
	8. Inequality Property: If $a = b + c$ and $c > 0$, then $a > b$

Problem 4

1. Prove the Triangle Exterior Angle Theorem using a proof by contradiction. The reasons for the first part of the proof are provided. Write each step of the proof.

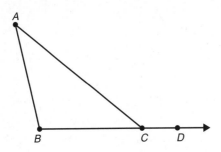

Given: Triangle *ABC* with exterior ∠*ACD*

Prove: $m\angle ACD > m\angle A$

Statements	Reasons
	1. Given
	2. Negation of Conclusion
	3. Triangle Sum Theorem
	4. Linear Pair Postulate
	5. Definition of Linear Pair
	6. Substitution using equations from steps 2 and 5
	7. Substitution using equations from steps 3 and 6
	8. Angle Subtraction
	9. Angle Subtraction
	10. Definition of Triangle

5

2. Prove the Triangle Exterior Angle Theorem using a proof by contradiction. The reasons for the second part of the proof are provided. Write each step of the proof.

Given: Triangle ABC with exterior $\angle ACD$

Prove: $m\angle ACD > m\angle B$

Statements	Reasons
	1. Given
	2. Negation of Conclusion
	3. Triangle Sum Theorem
	4. Linear Pair Postulate
	5. Definition of Linear Pair
	6. Substitution using equations from steps 2 and 5
	7. Substitution using equations from steps 3 and 6
	8. Angle Subtraction
	9. Angle Subtraction
	10. Definition of Triangle

5

Problem 5

1. Complete the direct proof.

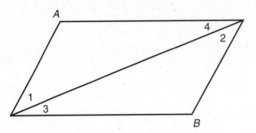

Given: $m\angle 1 = m\angle 2$, $m\angle 4 = m\angle 3$

Prove: $m\angle A = m\angle B$

Statements	Reasons

2. Complete the proof from Question 1 using an indirect proof.

Given: $m\angle 1 = m\angle 2$, $m\angle 4 = m\angle 3$

Prove: $m\angle A = m\angle B$

Statements	Reasons

Be prepared to share your solutions and methods.

5

5

Objectives

In this lesson you will:

- Prove the Side-Side-Side (SSS) Congruence Theorem.
- Use given information to show that two triangles are congruent.

Key Terms

- Side-Side-Side Congruence Theorem
- Side-Angle-Side Congruence Theorem
- paragraph proof

In three-dimensional computer graphics, a triangle is one of the shapes that is used to create realistic graphics.

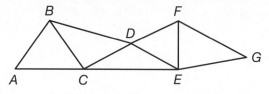

Problem 1 Constructing the Strip

To make the file size that contains the graphic smaller and to make the graphic display faster, *triangle strips* in the graphic are identified. A triangle strip is a list of triangles that share vertices. A triangle strip is shown.

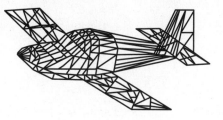

A. Identify the vertices that are shared by triangles in this triangle strip.

B. For each triangle, identify the number of vertices that are shared with another triangle.

© 2009 Carnegie Learning, Inc.

5

C. For each triangle, identify the number of sides that are shared with another triangle.

D. Consider this triangle. Use a compass and a straightedge to create a triangle strip of two triangles in the following way. Open your compass to the length of $\overline{AC}$. Place the compass point on point A and draw an arc to the left of $\overline{AB}$. Now open your compass to the length of $\overline{BC}$. Place the compass point on point B and draw an arc to the left of $\overline{AB}$ so that it intersects the first arc. Label the intersection of the arcs as point D. Then use your straight edge to draw $\overline{AD}$ and $\overline{BD}$.

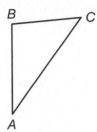

E. Without measuring, how do the lengths of the sides of $\triangle ABC$ and $\triangle ADB$ compare? How do you know?

Use a ruler to verify your answer.

F. Use a protractor to measure the interior angles of the triangles. What can you conclude about the triangles?

5

Investigate Problem 1

1. Suppose that you have three line segments with fixed lengths and you make a triangle with these three line segments. Is it possible to form a new triangle from the same three line segments whose corresponding angles are not congruent to angles of the original triangle? Why or why not?

2. If the corresponding sides of two triangles are congruent, what can you conclude about the corresponding angles of the triangles? Explain your reasoning.

If you know that the corresponding sides of two triangles are congruent, then the triangles are congruent. This result is called the **Side-Side-Side (SSS) Congruence Theorem.**

3. How does the SSS Congruence Theorem follow from the SSS Similarity Postulate?

5

Complete the two-column proof of the SSS Congruence Theorem.

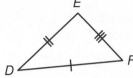

Statements	Reasons
1. $\overline{AC} \cong \overline{DF}$, $\overline{AB} \cong \overline{DE}$, $\overline{BC} \cong \overline{EF}$	1. _____
2. $AC = \boxed{}$, $\boxed{} = DE$, $BC = \boxed{}$	2. Definition of Congruence
3. $\dfrac{AC}{DF} = \boxed{}$, $\dfrac{AB}{DE} = \boxed{}$, $\dfrac{BC}{EF} = \boxed{}$	3. Division Property of Equality
4. $\dfrac{\boxed{}}{DF} = \dfrac{AB}{\boxed{}} = \dfrac{BC}{\boxed{}}$	4. Transitive Property of Equality
5. $\triangle ABC \sim \triangle DEF$	5. _____
6. $\angle A \cong \boxed{}$, $\boxed{} = \angle E$, $\angle C \cong \boxed{}$	6. Definition of similar triangles
7. $\triangle ABC \cong \triangle DEF$	7. Definition of congruence

4. Two sides of one triangle are congruent to two sides of another triangle, and the angles formed by these sides are congruent. Draw and label a diagram of this situation. Be sure to name the vertices of the triangles.

What do you know about the ratios of the lengths of the corresponding congruent sides?

Are the triangles similar? Why or why not?

Are the corresponding angles of the triangles congruent? Why or why not?

Write ratios that compare the lengths of the corresponding sides of the triangles. Are these ratios equal? Why or why not?

Are the triangles congruent? Why or why not?

5. Write a congruence theorem that follows from the SAS Similarity Postulate.

Use this figure to complete the statement of this theorem, the **Side-Angle-Side (SAS) Congruence Theorem,** in symbols.

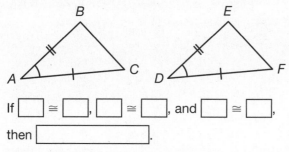

If ☐ ≅ ☐, ☐ ≅ ☐, and ☐ ≅ ☐,

then ☐.

You can use an argument similar to the one in Question 3 to prove the SAS Congruence Theorem.

6. A triangle strip is shown. Use a **paragraph proof** to show that ΔKLM is congruent to ΔQPN. Then use a paragraph proof to show that ΔMLP is congruent to ΔNPL.

Be prepared to share your solutions and methods.

5.6 Wind Triangles
Proving Triangles Congruent: ASA and AAS

Objectives

In this lesson you will:

- Use given information to show that two triangles are congruent.
- Determine whether there is enough information given to determine whether two triangles are congruent.

Key Terms

- Angle-Side-Angle Congruence Postulate
- Angle-Angle-Side Congruence Theorem

When airplanes fly from one destination to another, their exact course and speed are determined by the speed of the wind in the air and the direction of the wind. The calculation of the course involves a triangle called a *wind triangle*. In the wind triangle shown, the true course is the straight line from the starting point to the destination. The true heading is the course that must be flown to account for the wind in order to arrive at the destination. The last leg of the triangle shows the direction of the wind. The arrows indicate direction.

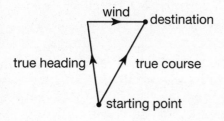

5

Problem I   Constructing Wind Triangles

In this grid, one square represents a square that is 10 knots by 10 knots. A *knot* is a unit that is used to measure speed in nautical miles per hour. The velocity vector from *X* to *Y* represents a true heading of 020°. The velocity vector from *X* to *Z* represents a true course of 050°. The velocity vector from *Y* to *Z* represents a wind direction of 090°. Notice that we use three digits to write the angle measurements.

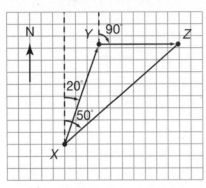

A. An airplane starts out at *A*, and its true heading is 030°. This means that the true heading is 30° clockwise of true north, shown in the upper left corner in the grid. Place the center of your protractor along the vertical line that passes through *A*. Line up the bottom of the protractor with *A*. On the grid mark 30° clockwise from true north.

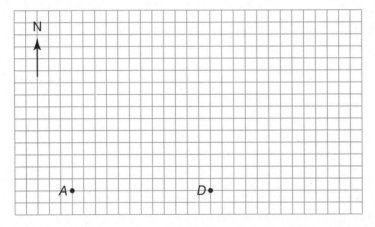

The plane is traveling at a speed of 100 knots. Open your compass to measure 100 knots on the grid. Then place the point of your compass at *A* and draw an arc that is above *A*. Then draw a velocity vector from *A* to the arc that passes through your 30° mark. This velocity vector is your true heading. Mark the unknown endpoint as *B*.

B. The true course is 040°. Place the center of your protractor along the vertical line that passes through *A*. Line up the bottom of the protractor with *A*. On the grid mark 40° clockwise from true north and draw a velocity vector that starts at *A* and passes through your mark.

C. The wind direction is 080°. Place the center of your protractor along the vertical line that passes through *B*. Line up the bottom of the protractor with *B*. On the grid mark 80° clockwise from true north and draw a line segment that starts at *B* and passes through your mark and meets the velocity vector from part (B). Label the last vertex as *C*.

D. Determine the measure of ∠*BAC* without using your protractor. Show all your work and label this angle on the triangle.

E. Label the length of $\overline{AB}$ on the triangle.

F. Determine the measure of ∠*CBA*. Show all your work and label this angle on the triangle. Hint: Draw a diagram of the triangle and draw vertical velocity vectors through *A* and *B*. Then use what you know about the measures of the angles formed by parallel lines and a transversal.

G. Another airplane starts out at point *D*. Its true heading is 040° and its speed is 100 knots. The true course of this plane is 050°. The wind direction is 090°. Follow the steps you used to draw △*ABC* to draw the wind triangle for this airplane on the grid in part A. Label the other vertices of this triangle as *E* and *F*.

H. Compare the side lengths and interior angle measures of △*ABC* and △*DEF*. What do you notice?

I. What information about both triangles' sides and angles did you need to know in order to draw the triangles?

How does this information in the triangles compare?

Investigate Problem 1

1. The result of Problem 1 is called the *Angle-Side-Angle (ASA) Congruence Postulate*.

> ### Angle-Side-Angle (ASA) Congruence Postulate
> If two angles of one triangle are congruent to two angles of another triangle and the included sides are congruent, then the triangles are congruent.
>
>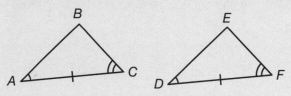
>
> If $\angle A \cong \angle D$, $\angle C \cong \angle F$, and $\overline{AC} \cong \overline{DF}$, then $\triangle ABC \cong \triangle DEF$.

Which of the similarity postulates do you think that this postulate is related to? Explain your reasoning.

2. Use the given information to show that $\triangle LMP \cong \triangle NMP$. Explain your reasoning.

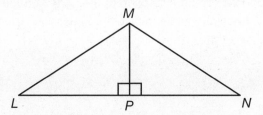

$\overline{MP}$ is the angle bisector of $\angle LMN$.

Problem 2   Different Sides and Different Angles

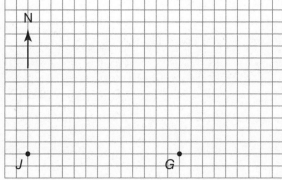

A. An airplane is starting from G. Its true heading is 015° and its speed is 80 knots. Draw the true heading and label its length on the grid. Label the unknown endpoint as H.

B. The true course is 040°. Draw a velocity vector on the grid that represents the true course. Label the measure of $\angle G$ on the grid.

C. The angle between the wind direction and the true course is 40°. Can you use this information to determine the location of the last vertex of the wind triangle? If so, determine the location of the vertex on the grid and label the point as *I*. Label the angle measure you used to determine *I* on the grid. Explain your method.

D. Another airplane is starting from *J*. Its true heading is 035° and its speed is 80 knots. Draw the true heading and label its length on the grid and label the unknown endpoint as *K*.

E. The angle between this airplane's true heading and true course is the same as that of the airplane in part (A) through part (C). What is the true course?

Draw a line segment on the grid that represents the true course. Label the measure of ∠*J* on the grid.

F. The wind direction is 100°. Use the location of *K* to determine the location of the last vertex on the grid and label this point as *L*.

5

Investigate Problem 2

1. Compare the side lengths and interior angle measures of △GHI and △JKL. What do you notice?

2. What information did you have about the triangles in order to draw them?

3. If two angles of one triangle are congruent to two angles of another triangle, what other piece of information do you need to know in order to conclude that the triangles are congruent? Explain your reasoning.

4. The ASA Congruence Postulate allows you to develop the *Angle-Angle-Side (AAS) Congruence Theorem*.

   ## Angle-Angle-Side (AAS) Congruence Theorem
   If two angles of one triangle are congruent to two angles of another triangle and two corresponding non-included sides are congruent, then the triangles are congruent.

   Complete the statement of this theorem in symbols.

   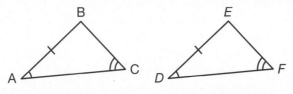

   If ∠A ≅ ☐, ☐ ≅ ∠F, and $\overline{AB}$ ≅ ☐,

   then ☐.

   This theorem can be proved by using the Angle-Angle-Side (AAS) Congruence Theorem.

5. Can you use the information given in the figure to show that $\triangle STR \cong \triangle VTU$ If so, explain how. If not, explain why not.

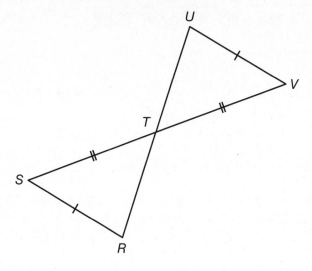

 Be prepared to share your solutions and methods.

5

5.7   Planting Grape Vines
Proving Triangles Congruent: HL

Objectives

In this lesson you will:

- Use given information to show that two triangles are congruent.
- Prove the Hypotenuse-Leg (HL) Congruence Theorem.

Key Term

- Hypotenuse-Leg Congruence Theorem

At a vineyard, grape vines are planted in straight rows that are parallel to each other. Vertical posts are erected along a row, and horizontal wires are attached to these posts so that the vines can grow along these wires.

Problem 1   Locating the Row

After the first row is in place, the people that are erecting the posts can make sure that the rows are straight and are parallel to each other by using right triangles.

Right triangles are used to locate the positions of markers that will be used to ensure that the end posts of each row lie in straight lines. These markers are also the locations of the end posts of a row. This figure shows an overhead view of the vineyard.

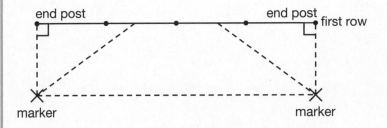

A. In order for the first row and the row formed by the markers to be parallel, what must be true about the distances between the markers and the end posts?

B. In order for the first row and the row formed by the markers to be parallel, what must be true about the triangles used to determine the locations of the markers?

Investigate Problem 1

1. Two groups of construction workers needed to lay out two ninety degree angles on either end of a line between two posts. Each group was given three lengths of rope, 9 feet, 12 feet, and 15 feet long. One group laid the 12-foot rope on the line between the posts, then took the 9-foot piece from the left post and the 15-foot length from the other end of the 12-foot rope and walked them out until they met to form a triangle, as shown. The other group walked the 9-foot length of the rope from the right post straight toward the second row, making sure that the rope formed a 90-degree angle with the first row. They then took the 12-foot length from the post and the 15-foot length from the marker and walked them out to form a triangle as shown.

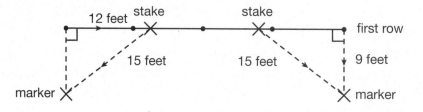

Are they right triangles? Are the triangles congruent? Justify your answers.

2. Two groups of construction workers needed to lay out two ninety degree angles on either end of a line between two posts. Each group was given three lengths of rope, 18 feet, 24 feet, and 30 feet long. One group laid the 24-foot rope on the line between the posts, then took the 18-foot piece from the left post and the 30-foot length from the other end of the 24-foot rope and walked them out until they met to form a triangle. The other group laid the 18-foot length of the rope from the right post straight toward the second row, making sure that the rope formed a 90-degree angle with the first row. They then took the 24-foot length from the post and the 30-foot length from the marker and walked them out to form a triangle.

Draw a diagram of the situation. Are they right triangles? Are the triangles congruent? Justify your answers.

3. Do you think that you need to determine the lengths of all three sides of two right triangles in order to determine that the triangles are congruent? Explain your reasoning.

5

4. If you know that two triangles are right triangles and the corresponding legs are congruent, how do you know that the triangles are congruent? Explain your reasoning.

5. If you know that two triangles are right triangles and a pair of legs is congruent and the hypotenuses are congruent, how do you know that the triangles are congruent? Explain your reasoning.

6. Complete this two-column proof to prove the *Hypotenuse-Leg (HL) Congruence Theorem*.

Hypotenuse-Leg (HL) Congruence Theorem

If the hypotenuse and a leg of a right triangle are congruent to the hypotenuse and leg of another right triangle, then the triangles are congruent.

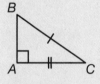 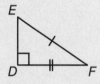

If $\overline{BC} \cong \overline{EF}$ and $\overline{AC} \cong \overline{DF}$, then $\triangle ABC \cong \triangle DEF$.

5

Statements	Reasons
1. $\triangle ABC$ and $\triangle DEF$ are _____.	**1.** Given
2. $\overline{AC} = \boxed{}$ and $\overline{BC} = \boxed{}$	**2.** Given
3. $\boxed{}$	**3.** Definition of congruence
4. $AB^2 + \boxed{}^2 = BC^2;\ \boxed{}^2 + DF^2 = EF^2$	**4.** Pythagorean Theorem
5. $AB^2 + DF^2 = EF^2$	**5.** _____ Property of Equality
6. $AB^2 + DF^2 = DE^2 + DF^2$	**6.** _____ Property of Equality
7. $\boxed{}^2 = DE^2$	**7.** Subtraction Property of Equality
8. $\boxed{} = DE$	**8.** Property of Square Roots
9. $\overline{AB} \cong \boxed{}$	**9.** Definition of congruence
10. $\triangle ABC \cong \triangle DEF$	**10.** _____ Congruence Theorem

Be prepared to share your solutions and methods.

5

5

6 Properties of Quadrilaterals

The earliest evidence of quilting is an ivory carving from the 35th century BC. It shows the king of the Egyptian First Dynasty wearing a quilted cloak. You will examine quilts formed by using tessellations.

6

Objectives

In this lesson, you will:

- Classify quadrilaterals.
- Name quadrilaterals and parts of quadrilaterals.
- Draw a Venn diagram that shows the relationships among quadrilaterals.

Key Terms

- tessellation
- parallelogram
- rhombus
- rectangle
- square
- trapezoid
- kite
- Venn diagram

Quilts are often made of repeating geometric shapes that form *tessellations*. A **tessellation** of a plane is a collection of polygons that are arranged so that they cover the plane with no holes or gaps.

Some quilts are created in a block pattern, such as the one shown. Copies of these blocks are created by sewing different patterns or colors together. Then the blocks are sewn together to form the quilt.

6

Problem 1   Describing Quadrilaterals

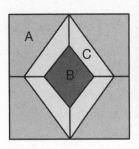
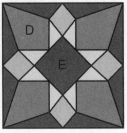
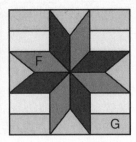

A. Shapes A through G labeled in these quilt squares are polygons. What is the classification for these polygons by the number of sides in the polygon?

B. How are these polygons the same? How are they different?

Investigate Problem 1

Use these quadrilaterals to answer the following questions.

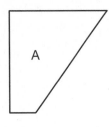
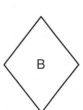
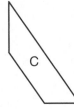

1. For each quadrilateral, use your protractor to determine which interior angles are right angles. Mark these angles as right angles on the quadrilaterals.

2. For each quadrilateral, use your protractor to determine which interior angles are congruent. Mark the congruent angles on the quadrilaterals.

6

3. For each quadrilateral, determine which sides are congruent. Mark the congruent sides on the quadrilaterals.

4. For each quadrilateral, determine which sides are parallel. Mark the parallel sides on the quadrilaterals.

5. Name the quadrilaterals in which both pairs of opposite sides are parallel.

These quadrilaterals are **parallelograms.**

6. Name the quadrilateral(s) in which both pairs of opposite sides are parallel and all the sides are congruent.

This type of quadrilateral is called a **rhombus**. The plural form of rhombus is *rhombi*.

7. Name the quadrilateral(s) in which both pairs of opposite sides are parallel and the interior angles are right angles.

These quadrilaterals are **rectangles.**

8. Name the quadrilateral(s) in which both pairs of opposite sides are parallel, the interior angles are right angles, and the sides are congruent.

These quadrilaterals are **squares.**

9. Name the quadrilateral(s) in which only one pair of opposite sides are parallel.

These quadrilaterals are **trapezoids.**

10. Which of the quadrilaterals has yet to be classified by its sides or angles?

Describe this quadrilateral in terms of its sides.

This quadrilateral is a *kite*. A **kite** is a quadrilateral in which two pairs of adjacent sides are congruent, but the opposite sides are not congruent.

6

11. Quadrilaterals are named by their vertices. For instance, this quadrilateral can be named quadrilateral *LMNP*, quadrilateral *MLPN*, but not quadrilateral *NLMP*.

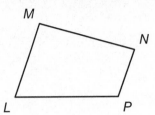

What does this tell you about how a quadrilateral must be named?

12. Draw quadrilateral *WXYZ* so that the quadrilateral is a parallelogram that is not a rectangle. Then name the pairs of parallel sides. Name any congruent angles.

13. Decide whether the following statements are true or false. Explain your reasoning.

All rectangles are squares.

All squares are rectangles.

All trapezoids are parallelograms.

All rectangles are parallelograms.

6

All squares are rhombi.

All quadrilaterals are parallelograms.

14. You can use a **Venn diagram** to show the relationship between different kinds of quadrilaterals.

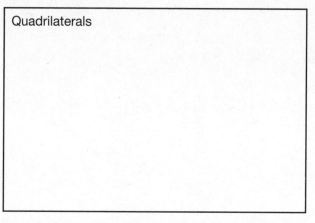

Quadrilaterals

First, inside the rectangle, draw a large circle that represents all parallelograms.

Now add a circle to the diagram that represents all rhombi. If no rhombus is a parallelogram, then draw the circle that represents the rhombi so that it is outside of the circle that represents parallelograms. If every rhombus is a parallelogram, draw the circle that represents the rhombi inside the circle that represents parallelograms. If some, but not all rhombi are parallelograms, draw the circle that represents the rhombi so that it intersects the circle that represents parallelograms.

Draw the circle that represents all rectangles. Then draw a circle that represents all kites. Then draw a circle that represents all trapezoids.

Complete the Venn diagram by labeling the part of the diagram that represents all squares.

6

6

Objectives

In this lesson, you will:

- Determine properties of kites.
- Determine properties of isosceles trapezoids.

Key Terms

- diagonal
- isosceles trapezoid
- base
- base angles

Simple kites are often in the shapes of simple geometric forms. A diamond kite is in the shape of a (geometric) kite, and a delta conyne kite is in the shape of a trapezoid.

Problem 1   Diamond Kites

A diamond kite and the outline of the kite are shown.

 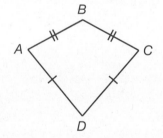

A. Draw a *diagonal* of the kite from vertex *B* to vertex *D*. A **diagonal** is a line segment that is drawn from a vertex to a non-adjacent vertex.

B. What is the relationship between △*ABD* and △*CBD*? Explain your reasoning.

C. Are ∠*A* and ∠*C* congruent? Explain your reasoning.

6

D. Can you determine whether ∠B and ∠D are congruent without measuring the angles? Explain your reasoning.

E. What do you know about ∠ABD and ∠CBD? What do you know about ∠ADB and ∠CDB? Explain your reasoning.

F. What does part (E) tell you about $\overline{BD}$?

G. Suppose that ∠B and ∠D are congruent. Then how does m∠ABD compare to m∠ADB? Explain your reasoning.

Because m∠ABD = m∠ADB, what kind of triangle is △ABD? Explain.

How does AB compare to AD? Explain.

Is this possible? Why or why not?

H. Complete the following statement:

If a quadrilateral is a kite, then only _____ of _____ angles are congruent.

6

1. The outline of the diamond kite is again shown. Draw both diagonals of the kite on the figure, and label the point of intersection as point *E*.

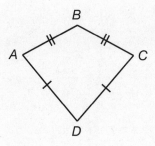

From Problem 1, we know that △*ABD* ≅ △*CBD*. We also know that $\overline{BD}$ bisects ∠*B*. What does this tell you about the relationship between △*ABE* and △*CBE*? Explain your reasoning.

What do you know about the relationship between ∠*AEB* and ∠*CEB*? Explain your reasoning.

Complete the following statement:

Angle *AEB* and ∠*CEB* form a _____ pair.

What can you conclude about *m*∠*AEB* and *m*∠*CEB*? Explain your reasoning.

Complete the following statement:

The diagonals of a kite are _____.

2. Consider $\overline{AC}$, the diagonal that connects the vertices whose angle measures are congruent. Where does $\overline{BD}$ intersect $\overline{AC}$? How do you know? Explain your reasoning.

What relationship does this give between $\overline{BD}$ and $\overline{AC}$?

6

Problem 2   Delta Conyne Kites

A delta conyne kite and the outline of the kite are shown.

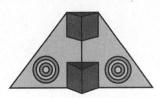

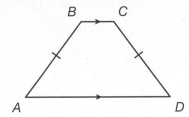

A. What do you notice about the nonparallel sides of the trapezoid?

This trapezoid is called an **isosceles trapezoid.**

B. How do you think $m\angle A$ compares to $m\angle D$? How do you think $m\angle B$ compares to $m\angle C$? Explain your reasoning.

Use a protractor to verify your answers.

C. Recall that the parallel sides of a trapezoid are the **bases** of the trapezoid. The pair of angles that share a base as a side are called a pair of **base angles.**

Name the pairs of base angles in the trapezoid.

Complete the following statement:

The base angles of an isosceles trapezoid are _____.

Label this information on the figure.

Investigate Problem 2

1. Draw the diagonals of the trapezoid on the figure in Problem 2. Then sketch △ABC and △DCB separately in the space provided. Mark any information on your sketch that you know about the relationships between angles and sides of the triangles.

What can you conclude about the triangles? Explain your reasoning.

Write a statement that tells what you know about the lengths of the diagonals of an isosceles trapezoid.

2. Complete this paragraph proof that shows that the base angles of an isosceles trapezoid are congruent.

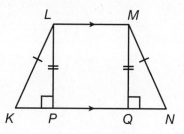

We are given that $\overline{KL} \cong$ _____ and _____ || $\overline{KN}$. First draw perpendicular line segments from vertex L and vertex M to _____ to form $\overline{LP}$ and $\overline{MQ}$. Segment $\overline{LP}$ and $\overline{MQ}$ are _____ because $\overline{LM}$ || $\overline{KN}$, and the distance between two parallel lines is the same from any point on either line. Angle KPL and ∠NQM are right angles because $\overline{LP} \perp$ _____ and $\overline{MQ} \perp$ _____. So △KLP and △NMQ are _____ triangles with a pair of congruent legs and congruent hypotenuses. By the _____ Theorem, △KLP ≅ NMQ. Because ∠K and ∠N are _____ angles of congruent triangles, the angles are congruent. Angle L and ∠M can be shown to be congruent in a similar way.

6

© 2009 Carnegie Learning, Inc.

6

6.3 Binocular Stand Design
Parallelograms and Rhombi

Objectives

In this lesson, you will:
- Determine properties of parallelograms.
- Determine properties of rhombi.

Key Terms
- opposite sides
- consecutive sides
- consecutive angles
- opposite angles

Sometimes, binoculars are better for viewing stars than telescopes. Because it is not reasonable for a person to hold the binoculars for an extended period of time, there are binocular stands that can be used to hold the binoculars. Part of the structure for this stand is in the shape of a parallelogram.

Problem 1 Holding It Steady

A typical binocular stand and an outline of the parallelogram part of the stand are shown.

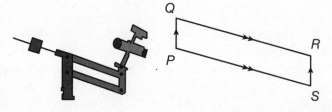

A. Two sides of a parallelogram that do not intersect are **opposite sides.** Name the pairs of opposite sides in parallelogram *PQRS*.

B. Two sides of a parallelogram that intersect are **consecutive sides.** Name the pairs of consecutive sides in parallelogram *PQRS*.

C. Two angles of a parallelogram that have a side in common are **consecutive angles.** Name the pairs of consecutive angles in parallelogram *PQRS*.

D. Two angles of a parallelogram that do not have a side in common are **opposite angles.** Name the pairs of opposite angles in parallelogram *PQRS*.

E. What do you think is the relationship between the opposite sides of a parallelogram? What do you think is the relationship between the opposite angles of a parallelogram? What do you think is the relationship between the consecutive angles of a parallelogram?

Investigate Problem I

1. The parallelogram from Problem 1 is shown. Draw the diagonal that connects vertices *P* and *R*.

How does *m∠PRS* compare to *m∠RPQ*? How does *m∠QRP* compare to *m∠SPR*? Explain your reasoning.

What can you conclude about △*QRP* and △*SPR*? Explain your reasoning.

What can you conclude about the opposite sides of a parallelogram? Explain your reasoning.

What can you conclude about ∠*Q* and ∠*S*? Explain your reasoning.

6

Can you draw a conclusion about ∠R and ∠S? If so, what is your conclusion? Explain your reasoning.

Which other pairs of angles have this same relationship?

Are ∠P and ∠R congruent? Explain your reasoning.

2. Complete the following statements:

   The opposite sides of a parallelogram are _____.

   The opposite angles of a parallelogram are _____.

   The consecutive angles in a parallelogram are _____.

3. Draw the diagonals on this parallelogram. Label the intersection point as point *T*. What do you know about the opposite sides of the parallelogram? Label this information on your figure.

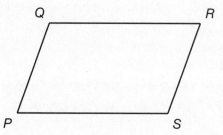

Use what you learned in Question 1 to name the congruent triangles formed by the parallelogram and a diagonal.

On the figure, label the congruent angles of the congruent triangles you named. What can you conclude about ΔQTR and ΔSTP? Explain your reasoning.

6

What can you conclude about △QTP and △STR? Explain your reasoning.

What can you conclude about $\overline{PT}$, $\overline{RT}$, $\overline{QT}$, and $\overline{ST}$? Explain your reasoning.

Complete the following statement:

The diagonals of a parallelogram _____ each other.

4. Consider this rhombus. Draw a diagonal that connects vertices A and C.

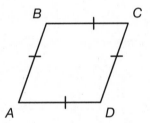

Take Note

Because a rhombus is a parallelogram, the properties of parallelograms are true for rhombi.

What do you know about △ABC and △ADC? Explain your reasoning.

What can you conclude about ∠BAC and ∠DAC? What can you conclude about ∠BCA and ∠DCA? Explain your reasoning.

How does $\overline{AC}$ relate to ∠A? How does $\overline{AC}$ relate to ∠C?

Complete the following statement:

The diagonal of a rhombus _____ a pair of opposite angles.

6

5. Consider this rhombus and its diagonals.

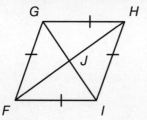

Triangle *GHJ* is congruent to △*IHJ*. Why?

How do *m*∠*HJG* and *m*∠*HJI* compare?

Triangle *GJF* is congruent to △*IJF*. Why?

How do *m*∠*GJF* and *m*∠*IJF* compare?

Triangle *GHJ* is congruent to △*GFJ*. Why?

How do *m*∠*HJG* and *m*∠*GJF* compare?

What is the relationship between ∠*HJG*, ∠*HJI*, ∠*IJF*, and ∠*GJF*? Explain your reasoning.

What does this tell you about the measures of the angles formed by the intersection of the diagonals? Explain your reasoning.

Complete the following statement:

The diagonals of a rhombus are _____.

6

6.4 Positive Reinforcement
Rectangles and Squares

Objectives

In this lesson, you will:

- Determine properties of rectangles and squares.

Fences built to keep livestock in enclosed areas are often built in rectangular sections. These sections are made stronger by adding one or two diagonal wire braces as shown.

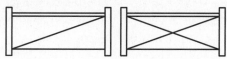

Problem 1 Making the Fence Stronger

A section of rectangular fence with two diagonal braces is shown.

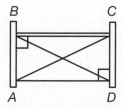

A. A rancher is building a section of fence that is 8 feet long and 5 feet tall between two fence posts. Label this information on the figure. About how much wire does the rancher need for each diagonal brace? Show all your work. Round your answer to the nearest tenth, if necessary.

B. What does part (A) tell you about the diagonals of rectangle *ABCD*? Is this true for all rectangles? Explain your reasoning.

C. Complete the following statement:

The diagonals of a rectangle are _____.

Investigate Problem 1

1. Do you think that the diagonals of every rectangle are perpendicular? If so, give an argument that supports your answer. If not, give an example that shows that the diagonals are not perpendicular. Explain your reasoning.

Take Note

Because rectangles and squares are parallelograms, the properties of parallelograms are true for these quadrilaterals as well.

Because squares are rhombi, the properties of rhombi are true for squares as well.

6

2. Do you think that the diagonals of every square are perpendicular? If so, give an argument that supports your answer. If not, give an example that shows that the diagonals are not perpendicular.

Summary   Properties of Quadrilaterals

In this chapter, you have learned the following properties of quadrilaterals.

- A **parallelogram** is a quadrilateral in which the opposite sides are parallel.

  The opposite sides of a parallelogram are congruent.

  The opposite angles of a parallelogram are congruent.

  The consecutive angles of a parallelogram are supplementary.

  The diagonals of a parallelogram bisect each other.

- A **rhombus** is a parallelogram with four congruent sides.

  A diagonal of a rhombus bisects a pair of opposite angles.

  The diagonals of a rhombus are perpendicular.

- A **rectangle** is a parallelogram in which the angles are all right angles.

  The diagonals of a rectangle are congruent.

- A **square** is a rectangle in which all four sides are congruent.

  The diagonals of a square are perpendicular.

- A **kite** is a quadrilateral in which two pairs of adjacent sides are congruent but the opposite sides are not congruent.

  In a kite, only one pair of opposite angles are congruent.

  In a kite, the diagonal that joins the vertices with the congruent angles is bisected by the other diagonal.

  The diagonals of a kite are perpendicular.

- A **trapezoid** is a quadrilateral in which exactly one pair of opposite sides is congruent.

- An **isosceles trapezoid** is a trapezoid in which the nonparallel sides are congruent.

  The base angles of an isosceles trapezoid are congruent.

  The diagonals of an isosceles trapezoid are congruent.

6

6

6.5 Stained Glass
Sum of the Interior Angle Measures in a Polygon

Objectives

In this lesson, you will:

- Determine the sum of the interior angle measures in a convex polygon.
- Determine the measure of an interior angle of a regular polygon.
- Determine the number of sides in a regular polygon given the measure of an interior angle.

Key Terms

- interior angle
- convex polygon
- regular polygon

Modern stained glass artwork and windows are created by cutting out pieces of glass and fitting them together with a metal strip that is grooved to hold the glass. All the metal strips that hold pieces of glass in a window or artwork are "glued" together by using molten metal.

Problem 1   Stained Glass Flowers

A stained glass design is shown.

A. Identify the different kinds of polygons that are in the stained glass design.

B. Draw one diagonal in the quadrilateral. What kinds of polygons are formed by the diagonal and the quadrilateral?

How many triangles are formed?

An **interior angle** is an angle that faces the inside of a polygon or shape, and is formed by consecutive sides of the polygon or shape. What is the sum of the interior angle measures of one triangle?

What is the sum of the interior angle measures of the rectangle? Explain how you determined your answer.

What is the sum of the measures of the interior angles of any quadrilateral?

C. Choose a pentagon from the stained glass design. Then choose one of the vertices from the pentagon and draw all of the diagonals that connect to this vertex.

How many triangles are formed by the diagonals?

What is the sum of the interior angle measures of one triangle?

What is the sum of the interior angle measures of any pentagon? Explain how you determined your answer.

D. Choose the hexagon from the stained glass design. Then choose one of the vertices from the hexagon and draw all of the diagonals that connect to this vertex.

How many triangles are formed by the diagonals?

What is the sum of the interior angle measures of one triangle?

What is the sum of the interior angle measures of any hexagon? Explain how you determined your answer.

E. The polygons that you have been considering so far are *convex polygons*. We are concerned only with convex polygons in this lesson and the next lesson. A **convex polygon** is a polygon in which no segments can be drawn to connect any two vertices so that the segment is *outside* the polygon. The polygon on the left is a convex polygon. The polygon on the right is not a convex polygon. Draw the line segment on the polygon that shows that it is not a convex polygon.

Investigate Problem 1

1. Explain how the sum of the interior angle measures of a triangle can be used to determine the sum of the interior angle measures of any polygon.

2. How does the number of diagonals that connect to a single vertex of the polygon relate to the number of sides in a polygon?

   How does the number of triangles that are formed by drawing all of the diagonals that connect to a single vertex of the polygon relate to the number of sides in a polygon?

3. What is the sum of the measures of the interior angles of a heptagon (seven-sided polygon)? Show all your work.

4. Write a formula that you can use to determine the sum of the interior angle measures of an *n*-gon. Explain your reasoning.

5. Use your formula to calculate the sum of the interior angle measures of a dodecagon (12-sided polygon). Show all your work.

6. Remember that a **regular polygon** is a polygon in which all sides are equal in length and all angles are equal in measure.

What is the measure of an interior angle of a regular pentagon? Explain how you determined your answer.

The measure of an interior angle of a regular polygon is 144°. How many sides does the regular polygon have? Show all your work.

6

6

6.6 Pinwheels
Sum of the Exterior Angle Measures in a Polygon

Objective
In this lesson, you will:
- Determine the sum of the exterior angle measures in a polygon.

Key Term
- exterior angle

You've probably seen a pinwheel like the one shown. This pinwheel was made by using a square piece of paper. We will use our knowledge of polygons to create our own pinwheels that are more complicated.

Problem 1   Making the Cut

Your pinwheel will be made by using a piece of paper that is cut into the shape of a regular pentagon.

A. What is the measure of an interior angle in a regular pentagon?

B. On a sheet of paper, use a protractor and ruler to draw the largest regular pentagon you can. Then cut out the pentagon.

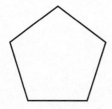

C. At each vertex, fold your pentagon so that the fold bisects the vertex angle, and then open the pentagon. Mark the point in the center of your pentagon where the folds meet.

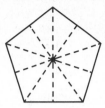

D. Cut along the fold at each vertex about halfway to the center. At the upper left corner of each flap, use a hole punch to punch a hole.

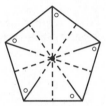

E. Carefully pull each corner with the hole toward the center of the pentagon. Then carefully put a push pin through the holes and then through the center of the polygon into the eraser head of your pencil. Your pinwheel is complete.

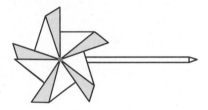

6

1. You may have noticed that when you were joining the flaps in the center, a pentagon similar to the one you started with can be seen. Look for the similar pentagon in your pinwheel.

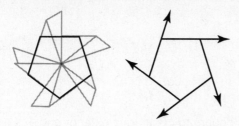

As with triangles, you can consider the **exterior angles** of convex polygons. Whenever you extend one side at a vertex, you create an exterior angle that is acute, obtuse, or right. Number the exterior angles of the pentagon on the right.

If one exterior angle is drawn at each vertex, how many exterior angles are there for the regular pentagon?

What is $m\angle 1$? Explain your reasoning.

What is $m\angle 2$? Explain your reasoning.

What is $m\angle 3$? Explain your reasoning.

What is $m\angle 4$? Explain your reasoning.

6

What is $m\angle 5$? Explain your reasoning.

What is the sum of the measures of the exterior angles of the regular pentagon?

2. Extend each vertex of this square to create one exterior angle at each vertex.

What is the measure of an interior angle of a square?

Determine the measure of each exterior angle. Explain how you determined your answers.

What is the sum of the measures of the exterior angles of a square?

6

3. Extend each vertex of this regular hexagon to create one exterior angle at each vertex.

What is the measure of an interior angle of a regular hexagon? Show all your work.

Determine the measure of each exterior angle. Explain how you determined your answers.

What is the sum of the measures of the exterior angles of a regular hexagon?

4. Without drawing a regular octagon, calculate the sum of the measures of the exterior angles of a regular octagon. Show all your work and explain how you calculated your answer.

6

5. Do you think that the sums you calculated in Question 1 to 4 are the same for any polygon, regular or not?

6. This pentagon is not regular. Extend each vertex of the pentagon to create one exterior angle at each vertex.

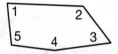

For each exterior angle, write an expression for its measure in terms of the measure of the adjacent interior angle.

Write the sum of your expressions and simplify the resulting expression.

What is the sum of the interior angle measures of a pentagon? Substitute this sum into the expression you wrote.

What is the sum of the measures of the exterior angles of any pentagon?

7. Consider any *n*-gon. Write an expression for the sum of the measures of the interior angles of the *n*-gon.

Complete the following expression for the sum of the measures of the exterior angles of the *n*-gon.

$$n \cdot \underline{\hspace{1cm}} - (n - \underline{\hspace{1cm}}) \cdot 180°$$

Simplify the expression to calculate the sum of the measures of the exterior angles of any convex polygon.

7 Counting Methods and Probability

Many good basketball players can make 90% of their free throws. However, the likelihood of a player making several free throws in a row will be less than 90%. You will use compound probabilities to calculate the likelihood of two or more events happening.

7

1. probability - measure of likelihood that an event will occur.

2. desired outcomes - outcome of event that has a favorable result.

3. outcomes - possible result of an event.

4. sample space - the set of all possible outcomes of an experiment.

5. compound events - event made of two or more simple events.

6. independent events - two events in which outcome of first event doesn't affect outcome of second event.

7. dependent events - outcome of one event affects outcome of another event.

8. without replacement - object is selected and not repeaced before another object is selected.

9. with replacement - objected is selected and replaced before another object is selected.

$$Both = \frac{56.25}{100}$$

$$Neither = \frac{62.5}{100}$$

$$Only 1 = \frac{37.5}{100}$$

7.1 Rolling, Flipping, and Pulling
Probability and Sample Spaces

Objectives

In this lesson you will:

- Calculate the probability of independent events with and without replacement.
- Calculate the probability of dependent events.
- Determine the sample space for independent and dependent events.

Key Terms

- probability
- desired outcomes
- outcomes
- sample space
- compound events
- independent events
- dependent events
- without replacement
- with replacement

Problem 1

In our daily lives, we encounter many instances of **probability.**

- The probability of rain today is 40%.

- A basketball player's probability of making a free throw is 75%.

- For a multiple-choice question with four answer choices, the probability of guessing the correct answer is one fourth.

Therefore, understanding the meaning and interpretation of probability is becoming increasingly important. With a partner:

1. Using fractions, interpret each of the probabilities listed.

$$\begin{array}{r} \overset{3}{\overset{2}{7.5}} \\ \times 7.5 \\ \hline 37.5 \\ 525 \\ \hline 56.25 \end{array}$$

$$\begin{array}{r} \overset{2\,'}{2.5} \\ 2.5 \\ \hline 125 \\ 50 \\ \hline 62.5 \end{array}$$

2. If the probability of rain is 40% for today and also 40% for tomorrow, then what is the probability it will rain both days? Neither day? Only one day?

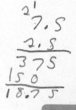

$$\begin{array}{r} \overset{2\,'}{7.5} \\ 2.5 \\ \hline 375 \\ 150 \\ \hline 18.75 \end{array}$$

7

3. The basketball player described has a "one and one," meaning that if she makes the first shot, she gets another shot. What is the probability that she makes both free throws? Only one? Neither?

4. Suppose a test were composed of eight multiple-choice questions, each with four answer choices. You guess the answer to each question. What is the probability you will guess the correct answer for the first two questions? For all of the questions?

Problem 2

The probability of an event happening is the ratio of the number of **desired outcomes** to the total number of possible **outcomes**, $P(x) = \dfrac{\text{desired outcomes}}{\text{possible outcomes}}$. A list of all of the possible outcomes is called the **sample space.**

1. One of the simplest examples of probability is the flipping of a coin.

   a. If a fair coin is flipped, what are the possible outcomes?

   b. What would be the probability of getting a head, $P(H)$? A tail, $P(T)$?

   c. If we flipped the coin again, does the probability of getting a head change? Explain.

   d. Suppose you flip a coin twice. List the sample space.

   e. What would be the probability of getting two heads? One tail and one head? Two tails?

   f. What is the sum of the probabilities you determined in part (e)? Are there any other possible outcomes?

2. Another example of probability is rolling a number cube with faces numbered 1 to 6.

   a. List the sample space if you roll the number cube once.

   b. What is the probability of rolling an even number, *P*(even)? A number greater than 2, *P*(greater than 2)?

3. Suppose you roll a number cube and then flip a coin. This is an example of **compound events** because it consists of two or more events.

   a. List the sample space for this event.

   b. What is the probability of rolling an odd number and flipping a tail? Rolling a 3?

   c. What is the probability of flipping a head?

4. A deck of playing cards consists of 52 cards with 13 cards in each suit: clubs, diamonds, hearts, and spades. Clubs and spades are black, and diamonds and hearts are red. Each suit is made up of cards from 2 to 10, a jack, a queen, a king, and an ace. You draw one card at random from a well-shuffled deck.

   a. How many possible outcomes are in the sample space? Do you need to list them all? Explain.

   b. What is the probability of drawing a king? A red card? A club? A red 10?

   c. If you draw an ace of diamonds and then put it back in the deck and shuffle the cards, what is the probability of drawing the ace of diamonds? Why?

7

The events described in Question 4 are *independent events*. In **independent events,** the outcome of the first event does not affect the outcome of the second event. In dependent events, however, the second event is affected by, or dependent on, the outcome of the first event.

5. Suppose you draw the 5 of clubs from a standard deck of playing cards. You do not replace this card, and you draw an additional card. You want to determine the probability that the second card will be a king. This problem is an example of determining probability **without replacement.** Had you replaced the 5 of clubs, it would be an example of determining probability **with replacement.**

   a. After drawing the 5 of clubs without replacement, what is the probability that the second card you draw will be a king? A black card? A club? A red 10?

   b. How do these probabilities differ from the ones in part (b) of Question 4? Explain.

Problem 3

Determining sample spaces can be time consuming and difficult when the spaces are large. Two methods for generating exhaustive sample spaces are using a tree diagram and using a table. Here is a tree diagram for the sample space for rolling a number cube followed by flipping a coin.

7

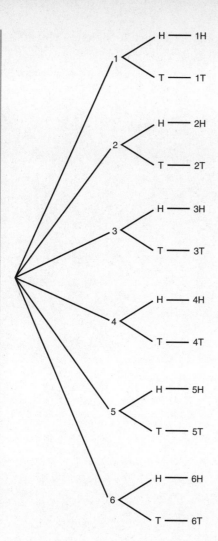

The sample space can also be shown in a table:

	1	2	3	4	5	6
H	1H	2H	3H	4H	5H	6H
T	1T	2T	3T	4T	5T	6T

1. How many outcomes are there for flipping a coin? How many outcomes are there for rolling a number cube? How many outcomes are there for the compound event of flipping a coin and rolling a number cube?

In many applications, two number cubes are rolled and the sum of the numbers is calculated.

7

2. Make a tree diagram for rolling two number cubes. Include the sum of each outcome.

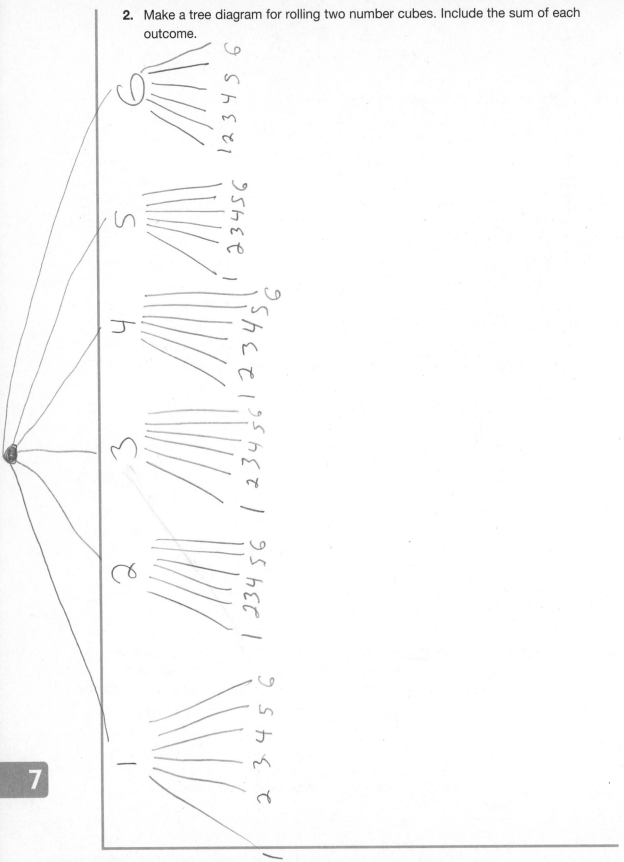

3. Construct a table for this sample space.

4. How many outcomes are there for rolling one number cube? Two number cubes?

6   then 36

5. You roll two number cubes. Use your tree diagram or your table to answer parts (a) through (d).

a. What is the probability that the sum is 7? 12? 2?

$7 = \dfrac{1}{6}$ $12 = \dfrac{1}{36}$ $2 = \dfrac{1}{36}$

b. What is the probability that the sum is greater than 8?

$\dfrac{5}{18}$

c. What is the probability that the sum is equal to or less than 5?

$\dfrac{30}{36}$

d. What is the probability that the sum is an even number?

$\dfrac{1}{2}$

7

6. If one event has 4 outcomes and another event has 10 outcomes, how many outcomes are possible for both events?

40 outcomes

7. What is the probability of an event that must occur? That cannot occur? Explain using the definition of probability.

100%

0%

Be prepared to share your work with another pair, group, or the entire class.

7.2 Multiple Trials
Compound and Conditional Probability

Objectives

In this lesson you will:

- Calculate compound probabilities with and without replacement.
- Calculate conditional probabilities.

Key Terms

- compound probability
- conditional probability

Problem 1   Number Cubes Revisited

In the last lesson, you determined the sample space and the probabilities involved in rolling two number cubes. Instead of rolling two cubes at once, we will look at what happens when we roll one, record the result, and then roll the same cube again.

1. Construct a table to show all of the possible outcomes from this experiment.

A compound event consists of two or more independent events. **Compound probability** is the probability of two compound events. Calculating compound probability depends on whether both the events must occur or whether either or both may occur.

7

2. Use your sample space from Question 1 and those from the last lesson to answer parts (a) through (j).

   a. How many different ways can the sum of two rolls be 7? List them.

   b. What is the probability of rolling a one on the first roll, $P(1)$?

   c. What is the probability of rolling a six on the second roll, $P(6)$?

   d. Based on your sample space in Question 1, what is the probability of rolling a one on the first number cube *and* a six on the second number cube, $P(1$ and then a $6)$? How does this result relate to your answers in parts (b) and (c)?

   e. What is the probability of rolling an even number on the first roll, $P(\text{even})$?

   f. What is the probability of rolling an even number on the second roll, $P(\text{even})$?

   g. What is the probability of rolling an even number on the first number cube *and* an even number on the second number cube, $P(\text{even} \text{ and } \text{even})$? How does this result relate to your answers in parts (e) and (f)?

   h. What is the probability of rolling a number less than 3 on the first roll?

   i. What is the probability of rolling a number greater than 4 on the second roll?

j. What is the probability of rolling a number less than 3 on the first number cube *and* a number greater than 4 on the second number cube? How does this result relate to your answers in parts (h) and (i)?

3. In Question 2, you calculated the probability of one event, rolling a 1, *and* the probability of a second event, rolling a 6. You also calculated the probability of rolling a 1 and a 6 on two number cubes. How are these situations similar?

4. Using your results from Question 2, if the probability of the first of one of two independent events is $\frac{1}{2}$, and the probability of the second of two independent events is $\frac{1}{5}$, what would be the probability of the first event and the second event occurring?

5. Use your sample space in Question 1 to calculate each probability.

   a. rolling a sum of 5 on the first roll of two number cubes

   b. rolling a sum of 9 on the second roll of two number cubes

   c. Using your answers to parts (a) and (b), calculate the probability of rolling two number cubes and getting a sum of 5 and then rolling them again and getting a sum of 9, *P*(5 *and* 9). Then calculate the probability of rolling two number cubes and getting a sum of 5 on the first roll *or* getting a sum of 9 on the second roll, *P*(5 *or* 9).

6. In general, if the probability of an independent event A, *P*(A), is *p*, and the probability of an independent event B, *P*(B), is *q*, then what is the probability of A *and* B, *P*(A *and* B)?

7

7. In general, if the probability of an independent event A, $P(A)$, is p, and the probability of an independent event B, $P(B)$, is q, then what is the probability of A *or* B, $P(A \text{ or } B)$?

Problem 2 Compound Probabilities

Calculate each of the following probabilities.

52

1. Using a standard deck of playing cards, calculate each of the following probabilities *with* replacement.

   a. P(ace *and* 10)

   $$\frac{4}{52} \cdot \frac{4}{52} \qquad \frac{16}{2704} \qquad \frac{8}{1352} \qquad \frac{4}{676} \qquad \frac{2}{338} \qquad \frac{1}{169}$$

   b. P(ace *or* 10)

   $$\frac{4}{52} + \frac{4}{52} \qquad \frac{8}{52}$$

   c. P(two diamonds)

   $$\frac{13}{52} \cdot \frac{13}{52} \qquad \frac{169}{2704}$$

   d. P(any pair)

   $$1 \cdot \frac{4}{52} \qquad \frac{4}{52}$$

   e. P(three of a kind)

   $$1 \cdot \frac{4}{52} \cdot \frac{4}{52} \qquad \frac{1}{169}$$

   f. P(three kings)

   $$\frac{1}{2197} \qquad \frac{64}{140608} \qquad \frac{32}{70304} \qquad \frac{16}{35152} \qquad \frac{8}{17576}$$

   $$\frac{4}{8788}$$

2. Using a standard deck of playing cards, calculate each of the following probabilities *without* replacement.

   a. P(ace *and* 10)

   $$\frac{4}{52} \cdot \frac{4}{51} \qquad \frac{16}{2652} \qquad \frac{16}{1326} \qquad \frac{8}{663}$$

   $$\frac{2}{4394}$$

b. *P*(ace *or* 10)

$$\frac{4}{52} +$$

c. *P*(two diamonds)

$$\frac{13}{52} \cdot \frac{13}{51} \qquad \frac{169}{2652}$$

d. *P*(any pair)

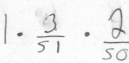

$$1 \cdot \frac{3}{51} \qquad \frac{7}{51}$$

e. *P*(three of a kind)

$$1 \cdot \frac{3}{51} \cdot \frac{2}{50} \qquad \frac{6}{2550} \qquad \frac{8}{1275}$$

f. *P*(three kings)

$$\frac{4}{52} \cdot \frac{3}{51} \cdot \frac{2}{50} \qquad \frac{64}{132600} \qquad \frac{32}{66300} \qquad \frac{16}{33150} \qquad \frac{8}{16575}$$

3. There is a homeowner's association with 25 members.

   a. A three-member pool committee needs to be established. Calculate the probability that Bill, George, and Rio are selected at random to serve on a committee.

   b. Calculate the probability that Bill is selected at random to be president, then George to be vice president, and then Rio to be treasurer.

   c. What is the difference between the situations in parts (a) and (b)?

   d. Calculate the probability of five particular members being chosen to serve on a five-member committee.

7

e. Calculate the probability of a particular member of the homeowner's association being chosen to serve as one of five officers.

4. The menu of a local restaurant allows you to choose from the following:

Appetizers: Shrimp, Veggies, Avocado Dip, Soup, Stuffed Mushrooms
Salads: Garden, Caesar, Pasta, House
Entrées: Steak, Pizza, Ravioli, Meatloaf, Chicken, Flounder, Spaghetti, Pork, Ham, Shrimp
Desserts: Ice Cream, Cookies, Fruit, Chocolate Cake, Pie, Cheese Cake, Sorbet

a. How many different dinners can a patron order if she must select one item from each category?

b. What is the probability that a patron selects chicken?

c. What is the probability that a patron selects meatloaf and chocolate cake?

d. What is the probability that one patron selects steak or another patron selects pie?

e. What is the probability that a patron selects meatloaf? Any entrée except meatloaf?

f. What is the probability that a patron selects flounder, Caesar salad, and fruit?

g. What is the probability that a patron selects pizza, cookies, and any salad except a garden salad?

h. What is the probability that a patron selects soup, chicken, any salad, and any dessert?

5. The probability that a basketball player makes a free throw is 60%.

a. If he is awarded two free throws, what is the probability that he will make them both? Neither? One?

b. If he is awarded three free throws, what is the probability that he will make all three? Two? One? None?

7

c. If he is awarded a one and one, meaning if the first is made then he gets a second one, what is the probability that he will make them both? Neither? One?

Problem 3

Terra and Jose are partners in math class. They are having a debate about the probability of rolling a total of 8 or more from two number cubes if the first roll is a 5.

Terra says that the probability is $\frac{2}{3}$ because once you roll a 5, the second roll can be a 3, 4, 5 or 6. So, the probability is $\frac{4}{6} = \frac{2}{3}$.

Jose says that the probability is $\frac{5}{12}$ because there are 15 ways to roll a total of 8 or more out of a total sample space of 36. So, the probability is $\frac{15}{36} = \frac{5}{12}$.

1. Is Terra or Jose correct? Explain.

2. Calculate the probability of rolling a total of 8 in two rolls if you already have a 5 on the first roll.

7.3 Counting
Permutations and Combinations

Objectives

In this lesson you will:

- Use permutations to calculate the size of sample spaces.
- Use combinations to calculate the size of sample spaces.
- Use permutations to calculate probabilities.
- Use combinations to calculate probabilities.
- Calculate permutations with repeated elements.
- Calculate circular permutations.

Key Terms

- factorial
- permutation
- combination
- permutations with repeated elements
- circular permutation

Problem 1   Strings and Factorials

Calculating large sample spaces can present several challenges because it is often too time consuming or impractical to list all of the possible outcomes. Even for relatively small numbers of options, listing the sample space can be challenging.

1. Using the first four letters of the alphabet, list all of the three-letter strings, such as DBA, that can be formed without using the same letter twice in one string (without replacement).

2. How many different strings are possible?

3. For each string, how many possible letters could be first? Second? Third?

4. How can your answer to Question 3 help you to calculate the number of possible three-letter strings?

5. How many different four-letter strings can be made using any four letters of the alphabet? Explain.

6. If you were able to use the letters more than once (replacement), how many three-letter strings could you list? How many four-letter strings? Explain.

7. If each letter could only be used once (without replacement), how many 10-letter strings could you list using the first 10 letters of the alphabet? Explain.

8. If you use the entire alphabet, how many three-letter strings can be made if each letter was only used once in each string (without replacement)? Explain.

9. Calculate the number of 26-letter strings possible without replacement. Explain.

10. In general, if there are *n* letters, how many three-letter lists are possible without repetition? Explain.

11. In general, if there are *n* letters, how many three-letter lists are possible with repetition? Explain.

In 1808, Christian Kramp introduced the **factorial,** which could help you to perform some of the calculations in the previous questions. The **factorial** of n, a non-negative integer, is $n! = n(n - 1)(n - 2) \ldots (3)(2)(1)$, the product of all positive integers less than or equal to n.

12. Calculate the following factorials.

 a. $5! =$

 b. $7! =$

 c. $10! =$

Take Note

Graphing calculators have a factorial key.

You can simplify fractions involving factorials by dividing out common factors.

For instance: $\dfrac{8!}{7!} = \dfrac{8 \cdot \overset{1}{\cancel{7!}}}{\underset{1}{\cancel{7!}}} = 8$

13. Simplify the following fractions.

 a. $\dfrac{8!}{6!} =$

 b. $\dfrac{11!}{9!} =$

 c. $\dfrac{7!}{4!} =$

 d. $\dfrac{7!5!}{8!3!} =$

14. Using factorials, rewrite your answers to the following questions.

 a. Question 4:

 b. Question 7:

 c. Question 8:

 d. Question 10:

7

Problem 2   Permutations

An ordered list of items without repetition is called a **permutation.** In Questions 1 through 4 of Problem 1, the three-letter strings are examples of permutations. There are a number of notations that are used for the permutations of n objects taken r at a time:

$$_nP_r = P(n, r) = P_r^n = \frac{n!}{(n - r)!} = n(n - 1)(n - 2) \ldots (n - r + 1)$$

1. Calculate the following permutations.

a. $_6P_3 =$

b. $_{10}P_1 =$

c. $_5P_2 =$

Take Note

Graphing calculators have a permutations key.

$_nP_r$

2. Using any 10 letters and the formula for permutations, answer the following.

a. How many four-letter strings can there be without repetition?

b. How many six-letter strings can there be without repetition?

c. How many one-letter strings can there be without repetition?

d. How many 10-letter strings can there be without repetition? (Note: In Question 12 of Problem 1, we already determined this answer.)

e. What conclusion must you make about the value of 0!? Explain.

7

Problem 3   Permutations with Repeated Elements

A friend asks for your help with a math problem. The problem asks how many different five-letter strings can be formed from the word START. Your friend thinks that this is a permutation of five letters taken five at a time. So, there are $_5P_5 = 5! = 120$ different 5-letter strings. However, the solution in your friend's math book is 60 different 5-letter strings.

1. Explain why the book is correct.

2. List all possible 3-letter strings that can be formed from each.

   a. ADA

   b. ABC

   c. AAA

3. List all possible 4-letter strings that can be formed from TOOT.

The permutations from Questions 1 through 3 are **permutations with repeated elements.** The number of permutations of n objects with k repetitions is $\frac{n!}{k!}$. The number of permutations of n objects with k repetitions of one object and h repetitions of another object is $\frac{n!}{k!h!}$.

4. Use the formula to calculate the permutations for Question 1.

5. Calculate the number of seven-letter strings that can be formed from the word Alabama.

7

Problem 4   Circular Permutations

A club consists of four officers: a president (P), a vice-president (VP), a secretary (S), and a treasurer (T).

1. List the different ways that the four officers could be seated at a round table

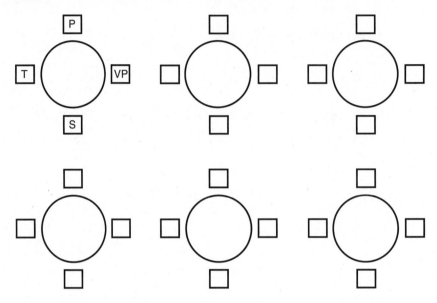

2. List the different ways that the officers could be arranged in a line.

3. Which elements from Question 2 are equivalent to the table seating of President, Vice-President, Secretary, Treasurer?

7

4. Which elements from Question 2 are equivalent to the table seating of President, Secretary, Vice-President, Treasurer?

5. Which elements from Question 2 are equivalent to the table seating of President, Treasurer, Secretary, Vice-President?

6. Based on Questions 3 through 5, how many equivalent elements are included for each seating arrangement? How does this number appear in the original problem?

The seating arrangement problem is a **circular permutation**. The circular permutation of n objects is $(n - 1)!$.

7. Calculate the number of table arrangements for each number of officers.

    a. Five officers

    b. Six officers

    c. Ten officers

7

Problem 5   Combinations

An unordered collection of items is called a **combination.** Problem 3 is an example of combinations. Different notations can be used for the combinations of n objects taken r at a time:

$$_nC_r = C(n, r) = C_r^n = \binom{n}{r} = \frac{n!}{(n - r)!\, r!} = \frac{n(n - 1)(n - 2) \ldots (n - r + 1)}{r(r - 1)(r - 2) \ldots (2)(1)}$$

1. Calculate the following combinations.

   a. $_6C_3$

   b. $_{10}C_1$

   c. $\binom{7}{3}$

2. Using an organization of 10 members and the formula for combinations, answer the following.

   a. How many four-member committees can be chosen?

   b. How many six-member committees can be chosen?

   c. How many one-member committees can be chosen?

   d. How many 10-member committees can be chosen?

7

Problem 6

1. State whether each question uses permutations or combinations. Then calculate the answer.

   a. Using a standard deck of playing cards, how many different five-card hands can be dealt without replacement?

   combination   2,598,960

   b. How many different numbers can be made using any three digits of 12,378?

   permutation   60

   c. How many different ways can you arrange 10 CDs on a shelf?

   permutation   3,628,800

   d. A professional basketball team has 12 members, but only five can play at any one time; how many different teams can be assembled?

   combination   792

2. Calculate the following probabilities.

   a. Using a standard deck of playing cards, what is the probability that a person is dealt a five-card hand containing an ace, a king, a queen, a jack, and a 10?

   2,598,960

   b. Consider the number 12,378. Using any three digits, what is the probability of making a three-digit number whose value is greater than 700?

   60

Be prepared to share your work with another pair, group, or the entire class.

7

7

7.4　Trials
Independent Trials

Objectives

In this lesson you will:

- Calculate the probability of two trials of two independent events.
- Calculate the probability of multiple trials of two independent events.
- Determine the formula for calculating the probability of multiple trials of independent events.

Key Term

- regular tetrahedron

Problem 1　Multiple Trials

A number cube has four sides painted red (R) and two sides painted blue (B). You roll the number cube twice.

1. List all possible outcomes.

2. Is there an equal probability of each outcome? Explain.

The two rolls are independent because what happens on one roll does not affect what happens on the other roll. The outcomes of a roll are mutually exclusive because the outcome can only be red or blue.

3. Calculate the probability of each outcome from Question 1.

4. What is the sum of the probabilities from Question 3?

5. How many different ways can you roll two reds? Two blues? One of each color?

6. What is the probability of rolling two reds? Two blues? One of each color?

7. You roll the same number cube three times. Calculate each probability using exponents.

   a. $P(3R)$

   b. $P(2R$ and $B)$

   c. $P(R$ and $2B)$

   d. $P(3B)$

8. What do you notice about the exponents and number of occurrences of each color from Question 7?

The probability of rolling two reds and a blue can be calculated in two different ways.

- Calculate the probability of a single outcome. Then multiply this probability by the number of ways that the outcome can occur.
- Calculate the probability of each outcome. Then add the probabilities.

For a small number of trials either method is relatively simple. For a large number of trials the first method usually involves less calculations than the second method.

7

9. Complete the table by listing all possible outcomes and the number of ways that each outcome can occur for each number of rolls.

Rolls	Outcome 1	Outcome 2	Outcome 3	Outcome 4	Outcome 5	Outcome 6
1	1R (1 way)	1B (1 way)				
2	2R (1 way)	R & B (2 ways)	2B (1 way)			
3						
4						
5						

10. The following is a different way to write the number of possible outcomes. Use a pattern to write the next two rows.

$$
\begin{array}{ccccccccc}
 & & & & 1 & & 1 & & \\
 & & & 1 & & 2 & & 1 & \\
 & & 1 & & 3 & & 3 & & 1 \\
 & 1 & & 4 & & 6 & & 4 & & 1 \\
1 & & 5 & & 10 & & 10 & & 5 & & 1
\end{array}
$$

The triangle in Question 10 is called Pascal's Triangle. It can be useful when calculating probabilities when the number of trials is relatively small. For example, calculate the probability of rolling 2 reds and 1 blue when the number cube is rolled three times.

To see what happens when the number cube is rolled three times, look in the third row of Pascal's Triangle. The four entries in the third row represent the number of ways to get 3 reds, 2 reds, 1 red, and 0 red, respectively. So, there are 3 ways to get 2 reds and 1 blue.

$P(2R \text{ and } 1B)$ = (Number of ways to roll 2 reds and a blue)
               (Probability of rolling 2 reds and a blue)

$$= 3\left(\frac{2}{3}\right)^2 \left(\frac{1}{3}\right)$$
$$= \frac{4}{9}$$

So, the probability of rolling the number cube three times and rolling 2 reds and 1 blue is $\frac{4}{9}$.

7

11. Calculate the probability of each outcome using a number cube with 4 red faces and 2 blue faces.

    a. Rolling 4 reds and 1 blue when the number cube is rolled five times.

    b. Rolling 3 reds and 3 blues when the number cube is rolled six times.

    c. Rolling 1 red and 6 blues when the number cube is rolled seven times.

Problem 2   A Formula for Multiple Trials

Consider the same number cube from Problem 1, consisting of 4 red faces and 2 blue faces. What if you wanted to calculate probabilities for 15 rolls, or 50 rolls, or 500 rolls? Using Pascal's Triangle to calculate the number of ways that an outcome can occur isn't realistic because you would have to write out 15, 50, and 500 rows, respectively.

  1. You can use combinations to make the problem easier for large number of trials. For three rolls of the number cube:

    ● Rolling three reds is the same as three objects taken three at a time.

    ● Rolling two reds and one blue is the same as three objects taken two at a time.

    ● Rolling one red and two blues is the same as three objects taken one at time.

    ● Rolling three blues is the same as three objects taken zero at a time.

    a. Calculate the equivalent combinations for each outcome of rolling the number cube three times.

    b. Compare the combinations from part (a) to the third row of Pascal's Triangle. What do you notice?

7

If the probability of event A is p and the probability of event B is 1 − p, then the probability of event A occurring r times and event B occurring n − r times in n trials is:

P(A occuring r times and B occuring n − r times)

For example, calculate the probability of rolling four reds and one blue in five rolls.

$$n = 5 \quad r = 4 \quad p = \frac{2}{3} \quad (1 - p) = \frac{1}{3}$$

$$P(4A \text{ and } 1B) = {}_5C_4 \left(\frac{2}{3}\right)^4 \left(\frac{1}{3}\right)^{4-3}$$

$$P(4R \text{ and } 1B) = \frac{5!}{4!1!} \left(\frac{2}{3}\right)^4 \left(\frac{1}{3}\right)$$

$$= 5\left(\frac{2}{3}\right)^4 \left(\frac{1}{3}\right)$$

$$= \frac{80}{243}$$

2. Calculate each probability.

   a. Rolling 3 reds and 3 blues when the number cube is rolled six times.

   b. Rolling 1 red and 6 blues when the number cube is rolled seven times.

   c. Rolling 3 reds and 7 blues when the number cube is rolled ten times.

   d. Rolling 3 reds and 4 blues when the number cube is rolled seven times.

3. A **regular tetrahedron** is a four-sided solid with each face an equilateral triangle. A regular tetrahedron has three sides painted blue and one side painted red.

   a. What is the probability of rolling a red?

   b. What is the probability of rolling a blue?

7

4. Calculate each probability for the regular tetrahedron from Question 3.

    a. Rolling five blues and two reds in seven rolls.

    b. Rolling four blues and one red in five rolls.

    c. Rolling five blues and five reds in ten rolls.

Be prepared to share your solutions and methods.

7.5   To Spin or Not to Spin
Expected Value

Objective
In this lesson you will:
- Calculate the expected value of an event.

Key Term
- expected value

Problem 1   First Round

You are a contestant on a game show. In the first round, the host gives you $200. You can choose to keep the money or give the money back and spin the wheel shown. You then win the amount at the top of the wheel when it stops spinning.

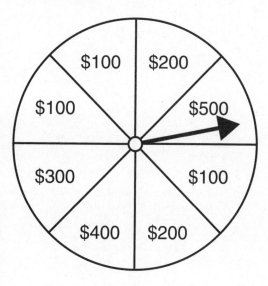

1. Would you choose to keep the $200 or spin the wheel? Why?

7

2. If you spin the wheel, what is the probability that you will win each amount?

    a. $100

    b. $200

    c. $300

    d. $400

    e. $500

3. If you spin the wheel, how often would you expect to win each amount?

    a. $100

    b. $200

    c. $300

    d. $400

    e. $500

4. Multiply each amount by the probability of winning that amount.

5. Calculate the sum of the values from Question 4.

The sum in Question 5 is the **expected value.** The expected value is the average value when the number of trials is large. In this problem, the expected value represents the amount that you could expect to receive from a single spin.

6. Based on expected value, should you keep the $200 or spin the wheel? Explain.

Problem 2   Second Round

In the second round of the game show you are offered another choice. The host gives you $300. You can choose to keep the money or give the money back and spin the wheel shown. You then win the amount at the top of the wheel.

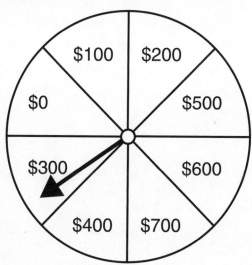

1. Calculate the expected value of spinning the wheel.

2. Should you keep the $300 or spin the wheel? Explain.

Be prepared to share your solutions and methods.

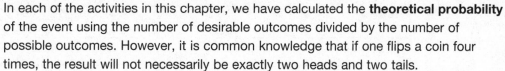

Objectives

In this lesson you will:

● Calculate experimental probabilities.

● Compare experimental and theoretical probabilities.

Key Terms

● theoretical probability

● experimental probability

Problem 1

In each of the activities in this chapter, we have calculated the **theoretical probability** of the event using the number of desirable outcomes divided by the number of possible outcomes. However, it is common knowledge that if one flips a coin four times, the result will not necessarily be exactly two heads and two tails.

1. Flip a coin four times or flip four coins once, and record your results in the Individual row in the table shown. Repeat this process 10 more times.

Outcome	4H	3H1T	2H2T	1H3T	4T	Total Flips/Trials
Individual						
Group						
Class						
Theoretical Probability						
Theoretical Result						

2. Gather the results from your group, and record them in the Group row.

3. Gather the results from your class, and record them in the Class row.

4. Based on your work earlier in the chapter, record the theoretical probabilities of each outcome.

5. Using the total number of trials for the class, calculate the theoretical number of times each outcome will occur, and record these numbers in the Theoretical Result row.

6. How do the theoretical results differ from the actual results obtained from the class? Why?

The result obtained from an "experiment"—an event or series of events—is called **experimental probability,** which is the ratio of the number of observed desired results to the total number of trials.

Problem 2

1. Roll two number cubes 36 times, and calculate the sum of each roll. Record your results in the Individual row in the table shown.

Outcome	2	3	4	5	6	7	8	9	10	11	12	Total Rolls/Trials
Individual												
Group												
Class												
Theoretical Probability												
Theoretical Result												

2. Gather the results from your group, and record them in the Group row.

3. Gather the results from your class, and record them in the Class row.

4. Based on your work earlier in the chapter, record the theoretical probabilities of each outcome.

5. Using the total number of trials for the class, calculate the theoretical number of times each outcome will occur, and record these numbers in the Theoretical Result row.

6. How do the theoretical results differ from the actual result obtained from the class? Why?

Problem 3   What's in the Bag?

Your teacher will provide each group with a numbered paper bag containing some items. DO NOT LOOK IN THE BAGS!

1. Your task is to determine what the items are and how many of each item is in the bag:

   ● Take only one item at a time.

   ● Record the name of each item in the Name row of the table shown. Place a tally mark in the Tally row. Then replace the item in the bag, and shake the contents.

   ● Repeat this process 10 times. (Note that you record the name of the item only the first time it's pulled.)

   Next, use your tallies to guess the number of each item that is in the bag. Record your guesses in the Group Guess row.

   Make sure to record the number that is on each bag. Once you have completed this experiment, pass your bag to another group.

Bag #	Item #1	Item #2	Item #3	Item #4	Item #5	Total Trials
Name						
Tally						10
Group Guess						
Class Guess						
Actual Number of Each Item in Bag						

2. Repeat the process for another bag.

Bag #	Item #1	Item #2	Item #3	Item #4	Item #5	Total Trials
Name						
Tally						10
Group Guess						
Class Guess						
Actual Number of Each Item in Bag						

7

3. Repeat the process for another bag.

Bag #	Item #1	Item #2	Item #3	Item #4	Item #5	Total Trials
Name						
Tally						10
Group Guess						
Class Guess						
Actual Number of Each Item in Bag						

4. Repeat the process for another bag.

Bag #	Item #1	Item #2	Item #3	Item #4	Item #5	Total Trials
Name						
Tally						10
Group Guess						
Class Guess						
Actual Number of Each Item in Bag						

5. After performing these experiments for the four different bags, discuss your guesses. As a class, guess the number of each item in each bag, and record your results in the Class Guess row.

6. Finally, open the bags, and record the actual contents of each bag in your tables. How close to the actual contents were your group's guesses? The guesses based on the class data? Explain.

7

Problem 4

Many uses of probability are based not on theoretical probability, but on experimental probability, which includes some of the situations we examined in Problems 1 through 3.

1. Think about this statement: "There is a 40% probability of rain today." What does this statement mean? Why is this statement most likely based on experimental probability?

2. Think about this statement: "The probability that a first-year teenage driver will have an accident increases by 20% if there is another teenager in the car." What does this statement mean? Why is this statement most likely based on experimental probability?

Be prepared to share your work with another pair, group, or the entire class.

7

The Preliminary Scholastic Aptitude Test (PSAT) is taken by about 1.3 million high school sophomores and juniors every year. The test is comprised of three sections—Mathematics, Critical Reading, and Writing—each of which is scored on a scale of 20 to 80 points. The sum of these scores is called the Selection Index. You will use statistical methods to analyze PSAT results.

8

8.1 Taking the PSAT
Measures of Central Tendency

8

Objectives

In this lesson, you will:

- Create a stem-and-leaf plot.
- Determine the distribution of a data set.
- Determine the mean, median, and mode of a data set.
- Compare the mean and median for different distributions.

Key Terms

- stem-and-leaf plot
- distribution
- mean
- measure of central tendency
- median
- mode

You and your friends plan to take the PSAT (Preliminary Scholastic Aptitude Test). You learn that this test requires 2 hours and 10 minutes, is usually taken by students during their sophomore or junior years, and includes math, critical reading, and writing questions. You also find out that during the 2004–2005 school year, about 1.2 million sophomores took the PSAT.

Problem 1   How Did Your State Score?

A. The table shows the average PSAT score for each state. To analyze the scores, you can use a *stem-and-leaf plot*. A **stem-and-leaf plot** is a data display that helps you to see how the data are spread out. The *leaves* of the data are made from the digits with the least place value. The *stems* of the data are made from the digits in the remaining place values. Each data value is listed once in the plot. Complete the plot. The first data value, 39.3, is done for you

PSAT Scores				PSAT Scores		
39.3	NV	43.9	KY	47.3	AR	49.9	KS
41.1	GA	44.1	PA	47.4	AZ	50.2	CO
41.2	FL	44.8	CA	47.4	WV	50.8	IL
41.6	ME	45.0	VA	47.5	AL	50.8	MT
41.7	SC	45.1	NC	47.8	VT	50.8	WY
42.0	MD	45.4	CT	47.9	AK	51.5	MO
42.3	DE	45.9	NY	48.5	UT	51.5	NE
42.3	MS	46.0	NJ	48.9	OR	51.5	WI
42.3	OK	46.4	OH	49.0	WA	51.7	SD
42.5	RI	46.7	MA	49.1	TN	52.7	IA
42.8	LA	46.8	HI	49.7	MI	52.9	MN
43.0	NM	46.8	NH	49.9	ID	53.2	ND
43.6	TX	46.9	IN				

Stems	Leaves	Key
39	3	47 | 5 = $\boxed{47.5}$
40		
41	1 2 6 7 6	
42	0 3 3 3 5 8	
43	0 6 9	
44	1 8	
45	0 1 4 9	
46	0 4 7 8 8 9	
47	3 4 4 5 8 9	
48	5 9	
49	0 1 7 9 9	
50	2 8 8 8	
51	5 5 5 7	
52	7 9	
53	2	

Be sure to include a key that shows what the stems and leaves indicate. Complete the key in your stem-and-leaf plot.

B. How does the stem-and-leaf plot display the data?

C. What is the highest average score for a state? What is the lowest average score for a state?

D. Based on your stem-and-leaf plot, what would you estimate is the average PSAT score for the United States?

Investigate Problem 1

1. **Just the Math: Distributions** Rotate the page with your stem-and-leaf plot 90° in a counterclockwise direction so that the leaves go up instead of to the right. The way in which the data are distributed, such as being spread out or clustered together, is the **distribution** of the data. Describe the shape of the distribution that you see in your rotated stem-and-leaf plot.

The shape of the distribution can reveal a lot of information about the data. There are many different distributions, but the most common are symmetric, skewed to the right, and skewed to the left.

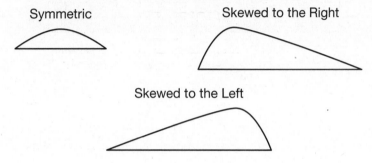

Symmetric

Skewed to the Right

Skewed to the Left

2. In your own words, explain how to draw each distribution.

3. What type of distribution does the PSAT score data have?

4. Is it easier to see the distribution in the stem-and-leaf plot or the table?

5. **Just the Math: Mean, Median, and Mode** The average PSAT score for each state is shown in order from least to greatest starting from the left. Locate your state's average PSAT score. Did the students who took the PSAT in your state do well?

PSAT Scores			
39.3	NV	43.9	KY
41.1	GA	44.1	PA
41.2	FL	44.8	CA
41.6	ME	45.0	VA
41.7	SC	45.1	NC
42.0	MD	45.4	CT
42.3	DE	45.9	NY
42.3	MS	46.0	NJ
42.3	OK	46.4	OH
42.5	RI	46.7	MA
42.8	LA	46.8	HI
43.0	NM	46.8	NH
43.6	TX	46.9	IN

PSAT Scores			
47.3	AR	49.9	KS
47.4	AZ	50.2	CO
47.4	WV	50.8	IL
47.5	AL	50.8	MT
47.8	VT	50.8	WY
47.9	AK	51.5	MO
48.5	UT	51.5	NE
48.9	OR	51.5	WI
49.0	WA	51.7	SD
49.1	TN	52.7	IA
49.7	MI	52.9	MN
49.9	ID	53.2	ND

One number that is often used to describe a set of data is the **mean** or arithmetic mean. The mean is also called the average. The mean is the sum of all the data values divided by the number of values in the data set. We write the mean as

$\bar{x} = \frac{\Sigma x}{n}$, where Σ is the symbol for the sum of all the x-values (data values) and

n is the number of values. What is the mean of the test scores in the table? Round your answer to the nearest hundredth.

46.75

Approximately what percent of the scores are above the mean? Approximately what percent of the scores are below the mean?

below = 46%

above = 54%

When we talk about a mean score, we are trying to determine a single value that best represents the performance of a group. This single value is a **measure of central tendency.** It is a value that represents a typical value in a data set.

6. Another measure of central tendency is the **median,** the middle score of the data, which is calculated by listing all the data values in order and determining the value that is exactly in the middle. Use your stem-and-leaf plot to determine the median score. Interpret this value in terms of the problem situation. Where does your state fit?

46.85

7. A third measure of central tendency is the *mode* of the data. The **mode** is the value in the data set that appears most often. If two values occur in the data set the same number of times, then each value is a mode and the data set is *bimodal*. If three values occur in the data set the same number of times, then each value is a mode and the data set is *trimodal*. Which test score appears the greatest number of times?

42, 3, 50, 8, 51.5

What is the mode of the test scores?

trimodal

8. Just the Math: Mean, Median, Mode, and Distributions When a distribution is symmetric, the mean and median are equal. How do you think the mean compares to the median in a distribution that is skewed to the left?

How do you think the mean compares to the median in a distribution that is skewed to the right?

Mean would be less than median

Draw representations of two sets of data, one for a distribution that is skewed to the left and one for a distribution that is skewed to the right. Then mark the possible mean and median on each distribution.

Take Note

When you have an even number of values in a data set, you can determine the median by calculating the mean of the middle two numbers. For instance, in the data set 12, 13, 15, 16, 18, 19, the median is the mean of 15 and 16, which is $\frac{15 + 16}{2}$, or 15.5.

8

9. This set of data is a set of PSAT scores from those students in a particular class at your school who took the test. Create a stem-and-leaf plot of the data and determine the distribution of the data. Then analyze the data by determining the mean, median, and mode. Show all your work. Finally, draw a representation of the data and mark the mean and median on the distribution.

Test scores: 36, 49, 16, 31, 21, 52, 29, 49, 48, 32, 42, 49, 44

16, 21, 29, 31, 32, 36, 42, 44, 48, 49, 49, 49, 52

Key
1	6
2	1 9
3	1 2 6
4	2 4 8 9 9 9
5	2

Key
1 | 6 = 16

Mean = 38.31

Median = 42

Mode = 49

10. Based on your results in Question 9, decide which measure of central tendency, the median or the mean, is the better representation of the test scores of the class.

The median because that's where the most numbers are.

8.2 How Many People?
Population Data and Samples

Objectives

In this lesson, you will:

- Analyze a large data set by collecting and comparing samples.
- Calculate the median and quartiles of samples.
- Construct box-and-whisker plots.
- Compare samples using box-and-whisker plots.

Key Terms

- sample
- absolute deviation
- average absolute deviation

Problem 1   Pick 'Em

The table at the end of this lesson lists the population of 542 cities and towns in Georgia in 2002.

1. List five characteristics of the population data.

2. A **sample** is a subset of a larger data set. Choose a sample of ten cities that you think best characterizes the data set. List those cities and their populations in the table.

City/Town	Population	Absolute Deviation from Mean	Absolute Deviation from Median

3. How did you decide which cities to include in the sample?

4. Calculate each measure of central tendency for your sample.

   a. Mean

   b. Median

   c. Mode

5. Calculate each quartile for your sample.

   a. First quartile

   b. Third quartile

6. Graph a box-and-whisker plot of your sample.

The **absolute deviation** is the absolute value of the difference between a data value and a measure of central tendency.

$$\text{absolute deviation} = |x_i - (\text{mean, median or mode})|$$

The absolute deviation can be used to describe the spread or variance of a sample.

7. For each data value in your sample, calculate the absolute deviation from the mean. Enter these values in the third column of the table from Question 2.

8. For each data value in your sample, calculate the absolute deviation from the median. Enter these values in the fourth column of the table from Question 2.

9. Calculate the **average absolute deviation** from the mean.

10. Calculate the average absolute deviation from the median.

11. Based on your calculations, what can you conclude about the population of Georgia's towns and cities?

Problem 2   Pick 'Em Again

As a class, decide on some criterion for choosing a second sample from the population data.

1. Choose a sample of ten cities using the criterion. List those cities and their populations in the table.

City/Town	Population	Absolute Deviation from Mean	Absolute Deviation from Median

2. Calculate each measure of central tendency for your sample.

    a. Mean

    b. Median

    c. Mode

3. Calculate each quartile for your sample.

    a. First quartile

    b. Third quartile

4. Graph a box-and-whisker plot of your sample.

5. For each data value in your sample, calculate the absolute deviation from the mean. Enter these values in the third column of the table from Question 2.

6. For each data value in your sample, calculate the absolute deviation from the median. Enter these values in the fourth column of the table from Question 2.

7. Calculate the average absolute deviation from the mean.

8. Calculate the average absolute deviation from the median.

9. Based on your calculations, what can you conclude about the population of Georgia's towns and cities?

Be prepared to share your findings with the class.

City Population for Georgia 2000 Census

	CITY	TOTAL		CITY	TOTAL
1	Abbeville City	2298	25	Arnoldsville	312
2	Acworth City	13,422	26	Ashburn	4419
3	Adairsville City	2542	27	Athens-Clarke	100,266
4	Adel City	5307	28	Atlanta	416,474
5	Adrian City	579	29	Attapulgus	492
6	Ailey	394	30	Auburn	6904
7	Alamo	1943	31	Augusta-Richmond	195,182
8	Alapaha	682	32	Austell	5359
9	Albany	76,939	33	Avalon	278
10	Aldora	98	34	Avera	217
11	Allenhurst	788	35	Avondale Estates	2609
12	Allentown	287	36	Baconton	804
13	Alma	3236	37	Bainbridge	11,722
14	Alpharetta	34,854	38	Baldwin	2425
15	Alston	159	39	Ball Ground	730
16	Alto	876	40	Barnesville	5972
17	Ambrose	320	41	Bartow	223
18	Americus	17,013	42	Barwick	444
19	Andersonville	331	43	Baxley	4150
20	Arabi	456	44	Bellville	130
21	Aragon	1039	45	Berkeley Lake	1695
22	Arcade	1643	46	Berlin	595
23	Argyle	151	47	Bethlehem	716
24	Arlington	1602	48	Between	148

	CITY	TOTAL
49	Bibb City	510
50	Bishop	146
51	Blackshear	3283
52	Blairsville	659
53	Blakely	5696
54	Bloomingdale	2665
55	Blue Ridge	1210
56	Bluffton	118
57	Blythe	718
58	Bogart	1049
59	Boston	1417
60	Bostwick	322
61	Bowdon	1959
62	Bowersville	334
63	Bowman	898
64	Braselton	1206
65	Braswell	80
66	Bremen	4579
67	Brinson	225
68	Bronwood	513
69	Brooklet	1113
70	Brooks	553
71	Broxton	1428
72	Brunswick	15,600
73	Buchanan	941
74	Buckhead	205
75	Buena Vista	1664
76	Buford	10,668
77	Butler	1907
78	Byromville	415
79	Byron	2887
80	Cadwell	329
81	Cairo	9239
82	Calhoun	10,667
83	Camak	165

	CITY	TOTAL
84	Camilla	5669
85	Canon	755
86	Canton	7709
87	Carl	205
88	Carlton	233
89	Carnesville	541
90	Carrollton	19,843
91	Cartersville	15,925
92	Cave Spring	975
93	Cecil	265
94	Cedartown	9470
95	Centerville	4278
96	Centralhatchee	383
97	Chamblee	9552
98	Chatsworth	3531
99	Chauncey	295
100	Chester	305
101	Chickamauga	2245
102	Clarkesville	1248
103	Clarkston	7231
104	Claxton	2276
105	Clayton	2019
106	Clermont	419
107	Cleveland	1907
108	Climax	297
109	Cobbtown	311
110	Cochran	4455
111	Cohutta	582
112	Colbert	488
113	Coleman	149
114	College Park	20,382
115	Collins	528
116	Colquitt	1939
117	Columbus	185,781
118	Comer	1052

	CITY	TOTAL
119	Commerce	5292
120	Concord	336
121	Conyers	10,689
122	Coolidge	552
123	Cordele	11,608
124	Corinth	213
125	Cornelia	3674
126	Covington	11,547
127	Crawford	807
128	Crawfordville	572
129	Culloden	223
130	Cumming	4220
131	Cusseta	1196
132	Cuthbert	3731
133	Dacula	3848
134	Dahlonega	3638
135	Daisy	126
136	Dallas	5056
137	Dalton	27,912
138	Damascus	277
139	Danielsville	457
140	Danville	373
141	Darien	1719
142	Dasher	834
143	Davisboro	1544
144	Dawson	5058
145	Dawsonville	619
146	Dearing	441
147	Decatur	18,147
148	Deepstep	132
149	Demorest	1465
150	Denton	269
151	De Soto	214
152	Dexter	509
153	Dillard	198

	CITY	TOTAL
154	Doerun	828
155	Donalsonville	2796
156	Dooling	163
157	Doraville	9862
158	Douglas	10,639
159	Douglasville	20,065
160	Dublin	15,857
161	Dudley	447
162	Duluth	22,122
163	Du Pont	139
164	East Dublin	2484
165	East Ellijay	707
166	Eastman	5440
167	East Point	39,595
168	Eatonton	6764
169	Edge Hill	30
170	Edison	1340
171	Elberton	4743
172	Ellaville	1609
173	Ellenton	336
174	Ellijay	1584
175	Emerson	1092
176	Enigma	869
177	Ephesus	388
178	Eton	319
179	Euharlee	3208
180	Fairburn	5464
181	Fairmount	745
182	Fargo	380
183	Fayetteville	11,148
184	Fitzgerald	8758
185	Flemington	369
186	Flovilla	652
187	Flowery Branch	1806
188	Folkston	2178

8

	CITY	TOTAL
189	Forest Park	21,447
190	Forsyth	3776
191	Fort Gaines	1110
192	Fort Oglethorpe	6940
193	Fort Valley	8005
194	Franklin	902
195	Franklin Springs	762
196	Funston	426
197	Gainesville	25,578
198	Garden City	11,289
199	Garfield	152
200	Gay	149
201	Geneva	114
202	Georgetown	973
203	Gibson	694
204	Gillsville	195
205	Girard	227
206	Glennville	3641
207	Glenwood	884
208	Good Hope	210
209	Gordon	2152
210	Graham	312
211	Grantville	1309
212	Gray	1811
213	Grayson	765
214	Greensboro	3238
215	Greenville	946
216	Griffin	23,451
217	Grovetown	6089
218	Gumbranch	273
219	Guyton	917
220	Hagan	898
221	Hahira	1626
222	Hamilton	307
223	Hampton	3857

	CITY	TOTAL
224	Hapeville	6180
225	Haralson	144
226	Harlem	1814
227	Harrison	509
228	Hartwell	4188
229	Hawkinsville	3280
230	Hazlehurst	3787
231	Helen	430
232	Helena	2307
233	Hephzibah	3880
234	Hiawassee	808
235	Higgston	316
236	Hiltonia	421
237	Hinesville	30,392
238	Hiram	1361
239	Hoboken	463
240	Hogansville	2774
241	Holly Springs	3195
242	Homeland	765
243	Homer	950
244	Homerville	2803
245	Hoschton	1070
246	Hull	160
247	Ideal	518
248	Ila	328
249	Iron City	321
250	Irwinton	587
251	Ivey	1100
252	Jackson	3934
253	Jacksonville	118
254	Jakin	157
255	Jasper	2167
256	Jefferson	3825
257	Jeffersonville	1209
258	Jenkinsburg	203

	CITY	TOTAL			CITY	TOTAL
259	Jersey	163		294	Lumpkin	1369
260	Jesup	9279		295	Luthersville	783
261	Jonesboro	3829		296	Lyerly	488
262	Junction City	179		297	Lyons	4169
263	Kennesaw	21,675		298	McCaysville	1071
264	Keysville	180		299	McDonough	8493
265	Kingsland	10,506		300	McIntyre	718
266	Kingston	659		301	Macon	97,255
267	Kite	241		302	McRae	2682
268	La Fayette	6702		303	Madison	3636
269	LaGrange	25,998		304	Manassas	100
270	Lake City	2886		305	Manchester	3988
271	Lakeland	2730		306	Mansfield	392
272	Lake Park	549		307	Marietta	58,748
273	Lavonia	1827		308	Marshallville	1335
274	Lawrenceville	22,397		309	Martin	311
275	Leary	666		310	Maxeys	210
276	Leesburg	2633		311	Maysville	1247
277	Lenox	889		312	Meansville	192
278	Leslie	455		313	Meigs	1090
279	Lexington	239		314	Menlo	485
280	Lilburn	11,307		315	Metter	3879
281	Lilly	221		316	Midville	457
282	Lincolnton	1595		317	Midway	1100
283	Lithia Springs	2072		318	Milan	1012
284	Lithonia	2187		319	Milledgeville	18,757
285	Locust Grove	2322		320	Millen	3492
286	Loganville	5435		321	Milner	522
287	Lone Oak	104		322	Mitchell	173
288	Lookout Mountain	1617		323	Molena	475
289	Louisville	2712		324	Monroe	11,407
290	Lovejoy	2495		325	Montezuma	3999
291	Ludowici	1440		326	Monticello	2428
292	Lula	1438		327	Montrose	154
293	Lumber City	1247		328	Moreland	393

8

	CITY	TOTAL
329	Morgan	1464
330	Morganton	299
331	Morrow	4882
332	Morven	634
333	Moultrie	14,387
334	Mountain City	829
335	Mountain Park	506
336	Mount Airy	604
337	Mount Vernon	2082
338	Mount Zion	1275
339	Nahunta	930
340	Nashville	4697
341	Nelson	626
342	Newborn	520
343	Newington	322
344	Newnan	16,242
345	Newton	851
346	Nicholls	1008
347	Nicholson	1247
348	Norcross	8410
349	Norman Park	849
350	North High Shoals	439
351	Norwood	299
352	Nunez	131
353	Oak Park	366
354	Oakwood	2689
355	Ochlocknee	605
356	Ocilla	3270
357	Oconee	280
358	Odum	414
359	Offerman	403
360	Oglethorpe	1200
361	Oliver	253
362	Omega	1340
363	Orchard Hill	230

	CITY	TOTAL
364	Oxford	1892
365	Palmetto	3400
366	Parrott	156
367	Patterson	627
368	Pavo	711
369	Payne	178
370	Peachtree City	31,580
371	Pearson	1805
372	Pelham	4126
373	Pembroke	2379
374	Pendergrass	431
375	Perry	9602
376	Pinehurst	307
377	Pine Lake	621
378	Pine Mountain	1141
379	Pineview	532
380	Pitts	308
381	Plains	637
382	Plainville	257
383	Pooler	6239
384	Portal	597
385	Porterdale	1281
386	Port Wentworth	3276
387	Poulan	946
388	Powder Springs	12,481
389	Preston	453
390	Pulaski	261
391	Quitman	4638
392	Ranger	85
393	Ray City	746
394	Rayle	139
395	Rebecca	246
396	Register	164
397	Reidsville	2235
398	Remerton	847

8

© 2009 Carnegie Learning, Inc.

	CITY	TOTAL
399	Rentz	304
400	Resaca	815
401	Rest Haven	151
402	Reynolds	1036
403	Rhine	422
404	Riceboro	736
405	Richland	1794
406	Richmond Hill	6959
407	Riddleville	124
408	Rincon	4376
409	Ringgold	2422
410	Riverdale	12,478
411	Riverside	57
412	Roberta	808
413	Rochelle	1415
414	Rockmart	3870
415	Rocky Ford	186
416	Rome	34,980
417	Roopville	177
418	Rossville	3511
419	Roswell	79,334
420	Royston	2493
421	Rutledge	707
422	St. Marys	13,761
423	Sale City	319
424	Sandersville	6144
425	Santa Claus	237
426	Sardis	1171
427	Sasser	393
428	Savannah	131,510
429	Scotland	300
430	Screven	702
431	Senoia	1738
432	Shady Dale	242
433	Sharon	105

	CITY	TOTAL
434	Sharpsburg	316
435	Shellman	1166
436	Shiloh	423
437	Siloam	331
438	Sky Valley	221
439	Smithville	774
440	Smyrna	40,999
441	Snellville	15,351
442	Social Circle	3379
443	Soperton	2824
444	Sparks	1755
445	Sparta	1522
446	Springfield	1821
447	Stapleton	318
448	Statesboro	22,698
449	Statham	2040
450	Stillmore	730
451	Stockbridge	9853
452	Stone Mountain	7145
453	Sugar Hill	11,399
454	Summertown	140
455	Summerville	4556
456	Sumner	309
457	Sunny Side	142
458	Surrency	237
459	Suwanee	8725
460	Swainsboro	6943
461	Sycamore	496
462	Sylvania	2675
463	Sylvester	5990
464	Talbotton	1019
465	Talking Rock	49
466	Tallapoosa	2789
467	Tallulah Falls	164
468	Talmo	477

8

	CITY	TOTAL
469	Tarrytown	100
470	Taylorsville	229
471	Temple	2383
472	Tennille	1505
473	Thomaston	9411
474	Thomasville	18,162
475	Thomson	6828
476	Thunderbolt	2340
477	Tifton	15,060
478	Tiger	316
479	Tignall	653
480	Toccoa	9323
481	Toomsboro	622
482	Trenton	1942
483	Trion	1993
484	Tunnel Hill	1209
485	Turin	165
486	Twin City	1752
487	Tybee Island	3392
488	Tyrone	3916
489	Ty Ty	716
490	Unadilla	2772
491	Union City	11,621
492	Union Point	1669
493	Uvalda	530
494	Valdosta	43,724
495	Varnell	1491
496	Vernonburgn	138
497	Vidalia	10,491
498	Vidette	112
499	Vienna	2973
500	Villa Rica	4134
501	Waco	469
502	Wadley	2088
503	Waleska	616

	CITY	TOTAL
504	Walnut Grove	1241
505	Walthourville	4030
506	Warm Springs	485
507	Warner Robins	48,804
508	Warrenton	2013
509	Warwick	430
510	Washington	4295
511	Watkinsville	2097
512	Waverly Hall	709
513	Waycross	15,333
514	Waynesboro	5813
515	Weston	75
516	West Point	3382
517	Whigham	631
518	White	693
519	White Plains	283
520	Whitesburg	596
521	Willacoochee	1434
522	Williamson	297
523	Winder	10,201
524	Winterville	1068
525	Woodbine	1218
526	Woodbury	1184
527	Woodland	432
528	Woodstock	10,050
529	Woodville	400
530	Woolsey	175
531	Wrens	2314
532	Wrightsville	2223
533	Yatesville	408
534	Young Harris	604
535	Zebulon	1181

8.3 Let's Compare!
Population and Sample Means

Objectives

In this lesson you will:

- Create samples of population data.
- Calculate sample means.
- Characterize populations using random samples.

Key Terms

- outlier
- random sample
- random number

Problem 1 Too Big!

1. Look up the population of the following cities using the population table at the end of the last lesson. Enter each population in the table shown.

City/Town	Population
Macon	
Athens-Clarke	
Savannah	
Columbus	
Augusta-Richmond	
Atlanta	

2. Is the sample consisting of these five cities representative of the population data? Explain.

3. What is the effect of including one of these cities in the mean? The median?

An **outlier** is a data value that is significantly larger or smaller than the rest of the data values. Sometimes it is useful to avoid including outliers in a sample so that the sample better represents the data set.

4. Does the population data set include any outliers that are smaller than the rest of the data values? Explain.

Problem 2 How to Choose?

As a group, decide on some criterion for choosing a sample from the population data.

1. Describe the criterion you used.

2. Choose a sample of ten cities or towns using the criterion. List those cities and their populations in the table.

City/Town	Population

3. Calculate the mean of your sample.

4. Collect the means of several other samples. List the means in the table from smallest to largest.

Sample Number	Mean	Sample Number	Mean	Sample Number	Mean

5. Calculate the mean and median of the sample means from Question 4.

6. The mean of the entire population data set is 5952. How does the mean of your sample compare to the mean of the entire data set?

7. How does the mean of the sample means compare to the mean of the entire data set?

Problem 3 Random Samples

It is difficult to choose a sample that is representative of the data set by picking data values by hand. A common alternative is a **random sample.** A random sample is a sample that is created by selecting data values randomly. When creating a random sample, each data value has an equal likelihood of being selected.

1. What is the probability of choosing each city in the population data set?

2. What is one method that you could use to create a random sample?

A **random number** is a number that is generated at random. Generating random numbers has been difficult historically. Now, technology such as a graphing calculator can be used to generate random numbers.

3. On a graphing calculator press the MATH key. Choose PRB and 1:rand. Press ENTER. This generates a random number between 0 and 1. Generate 10 random numbers between 0 and 1 and enter each in the first column of the table to four decimal places of accuracy.

Random Number Between 0 and 1	Random Number Between 1 and 535	City	Population

4. To generate random numbers between 1 and 535, multiply each random number between 0 and 1 by 535 and round to the nearest whole number. Enter the random numbers between 1 and 535 in the second column of the table from Question 3.

5. Look up each random number between 1 and 535 in the population data table. Enter the corresponding city and population in the third and fourth columns of the table from Question 3.

6. Calculate the mean of your random sample.

7. Collect the means of several other random samples. List the means in the table from smallest to largest.

Sample Number	Mean	Sample Number	Mean	Sample Number	Mean

8. Calculate the mean and median of the sample means from Question 7.

9. The mean of the entire population data set is 5952. How does the mean of your random sample compare to the mean of the entire data set?

10. How does the mean of the sample means compare to the mean of the entire data set?

Be prepared to share your methods and solutions with the class.

Objectives

In this lesson, you will:

- Collect and analyze sample data.
- Use sample data to make predictions and generalizations about population data.

Problem 1   Your Sample

As a class, choose some data that you would like to explore. Data might include ages of people in your town, heights of students at your school, and so on.

1. Collect ten data points. Enter each in the table shown.

Sample Number	1	2	3	4	5	6	7	8	9	10
Data Value										

2. Calculate the mean of your sample.

3. Based only on your sample and the sample mean, what can you predict about the population from which the sample was taken?

Problem 2   The Group Sample

1. Form groups of four students. Enter your sample and the samples of the other students of your group in the table shown. This is your group sample.

Sample Number	Data Value	Sample Number	Data Value	Sample Number	Data Value	Sample Number	Data Value
1		11		21		31	
2		12		22		32	
3		13		23		33	
4		14		24		34	
5		15		25		35	
6		16		26		36	
7		17		27		37	
8		18		28		38	
9		19		29		39	
10		20		30		40	

2. Calculate the mean of your group sample.

3. Based only on your group sample and the sample mean, what can you predict about the population from which the sample was taken?

Problem 3　The Class Sample

Collect the samples of every student in your class. Number the data values starting at 1. This is the class sample.

1.　Calculate the mean of the class sample.

2.　How does the mean of the class sample compare to the mean of your sample? To your group sample?

3.　Based only on the class sample and the sample mean, what can you predict about the population from which the sample was taken?

Problem 4　The Random Sample

1.　Using the class sample and a random number generator to create a random sample of ten data values. Enter each in the table shown.

Random Number										
Data Value										

2.　Calculate the mean of the random sample.

3. How does the mean of the random sample compare to the mean of your sample? To your group sample? To the class sample?

4. Based only on the random sample and the sample mean, what can you predict about the population from which the sample was taken?

5. Examine your sample, your group sample, the class sample, and the random sample. Which sample provides the best information about the population that you are analyzing? Explain.

Be prepared to share your methods and solutions with the class.

9 Function Transformations and Symmetry

The first well-documented postal system was in ancient Rome, where mail was carried by horse-drawn carriages and ox-drawn wagons. The US Postal Service delivers approximately 200 billion letters and 1 billion packages each year. Most businesses use both public and private mail systems to ship products to their customers. You will use graphs of equations to determine the effect of shipping costs on the total cost of purchasing machine tools.

9.1 Shifting Away
Vertical and Horizontal Translations

Objectives

In this lesson, you will:

- Translate graphs of functions vertically and horizontally.
- Write equations for translated functions.

Key Terms

- vertical translation
- horizontal translation

9

Problem 1   Moving On Up!

1. Graph each linear function on the grid shown.

   a. $f(x) = x$

   b. $y = x + 5$

   c. $y = x - 5$

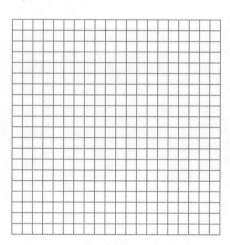

2. Graph each absolute value function on the grid shown.

    a. $y = |x|$

    b. $y = |x| + 5$

    c. $f(x) = |x| - 5$

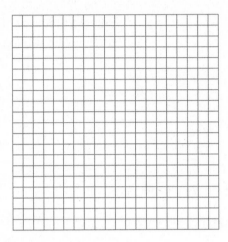

3. Graph each quadratic function on the grid shown.

    a. $y = x^2$

    b. $y = x^2 + 5$

    c. $f(x) = x^2 - 5$

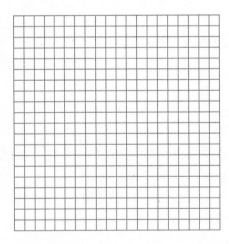

4. In Questions 1 through 3, part (a) is a basic function. What operation is performed to each basic function to result in the equations in parts (b) and (c)?

5. Describe how the graph of $f(x) + k$ is formed from the graph of $f(x)$.

A **vertical translation** of a graph is a shift of the entire graph up or down.

6. The graph of a function $g(x)$ is shown. Sketch the graph of

    a. $g(x) + 2$

    b. $g(x) - 4$

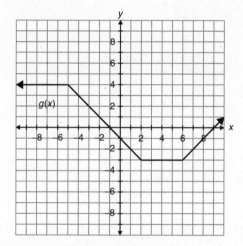

7. The graph of the function $h(x)$ is shown. Write a function in terms of $h(x)$ for each vertical translation shown.

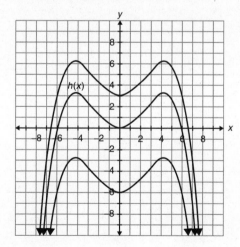

Problem 2   To the Left, to the Right!

1. Graph each quadratic function on the grid shown.

   a. $f(x) = x^2$

   b. $y = (x + 5)^2$

   c. $y = (x - 5)^2$

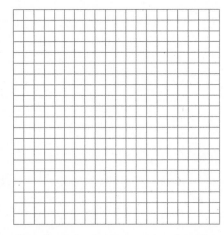

2. Graph each absolute value function on the grid shown.

   a. $y = |x|$

   b. $y = |x + 5|$

   c. $f(x) = |x - 5|$

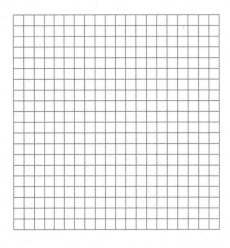

3. Graph each square root function on the grid shown.

   a. $y = \sqrt{x}$

   b. $y = \sqrt{x + 5}$

   c. $f(x) = \sqrt{x - 5}$

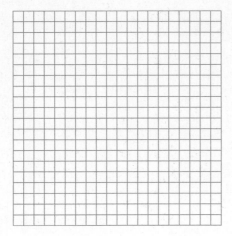

4. In Questions 1 through 3, part (a) is a basic function. What operation is performed on each basic function to result in the equations in parts (b) and (c)?

5. Describe how the graph of $f(x - h)$ is formed from the graph of $f(x)$.

A **horizontal translation** of a graph is a shift of the entire graph to the left or to the right.

6. The graph of a function $g(x)$ is shown. Sketch the graph of

    a. $g(x - 2)$

    b. $g(x + 3)$

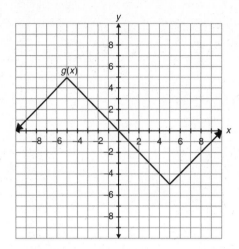

7. The graph of the function $h(x)$ is shown. Write a function in terms of $h(x)$ for each horizontal translation shown.

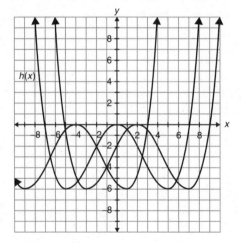

Be prepared to share your methods and solutions.

9.2 Expanding, Contracting, and Mirroring
Dilations and Reflections

Objectives

In this lesson, you will:
- Dilate graphs of functions.
- Reflect graphs of functions.
- Write equations for dilated and rotated functions.

Key Terms
- dilation
- reflection
- line of reflection

Problem I Dilating

1. Graph each absolute value function on the grid shown.

   a. $f(x) = |x|$

   b. $g(x) = 2|x|$

   c. $h(x) = 5|x|$

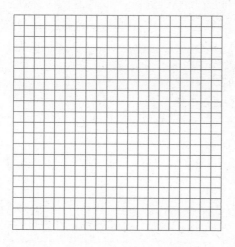

2. Complete the table to calculate the rate of change from 0 to 1 for each function in Question 1.

Function	Value at $x = 0$	Value at $x = 1$	Rate of Change
$f(x) = |x|$	$f(0) =$	$f(1) =$	$\dfrac{\Delta f(x)}{\Delta x} =$
$g(x) = 2|x|$	$g(0) =$	$g(1) =$	$\dfrac{\Delta g(x)}{\Delta x} =$
$h(x) = 5|x|$	$h(0) =$	$h(1) =$	$\dfrac{\Delta h(x)}{\Delta x} =$

3. Graph each quadratic function on the grid shown.

a. $f(x) = x^2$

b. $g(x) = 2x^2$

c. $h(x) = 3x^2$

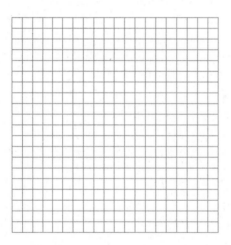

4. Complete the table to calculate the average rate of change from 0 to 2 for each function in Question 3.

Function	Value at $x = 0$	Value at $x = 2$	Average Rate of Change
$f(x) = x^2$	$f(0) =$	$f(2) =$	$\dfrac{\Delta f(x)}{\Delta x} =$
$g(x) = 2x^2$	$g(0) =$	$g(2) =$	$\dfrac{\Delta g(x)}{\Delta x} =$
$h(x) = 3x^2$	$h(0) =$	$h(2) =$	$\dfrac{\Delta h(x)}{\Delta x} =$

5. Graph each square root function on the grid shown.

a. $f(x) = \sqrt{x}$

b. $g(x) = 0.5\sqrt{x}$

c. $h(x) = 0.25\sqrt{x}$

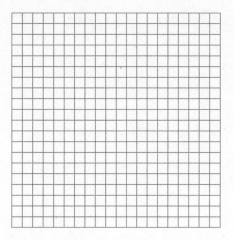

6. Complete the table to calculate the average rate of change from 0 to 4 for each function in Question 5.

Function	Value at $x = 0$	Value at $x = 4$	Average Rate of Change
$f(x) = \sqrt{x}$	$f(0) =$	$f(4) =$	$\dfrac{\Delta f(x)}{\Delta x} =$
$g(x) = 0.5\sqrt{x}$	$g(0) =$	$g(4) =$	$\dfrac{\Delta g(x)}{\Delta x} =$
$h(x) = 0.25\sqrt{x}$	$h(0) =$	$h(4) =$	$\dfrac{\Delta h(x)}{\Delta x} =$

7. In Questions 1, 3, and 5, part (a) is a basic function. What operation is performed on each basic function to result in the equations in parts (b) and (c)?

8. Describe how the graph of $a \cdot f(x)$ is formed from the graph of $f(x)$.

A **dilation** of a graph is an increase or decrease of the rate of change by a constant amount.

9. The graph of the function $f(x)$ is shown. Sketch the graph of

   a. $2f(x)$

   b. $0.5f(x)$

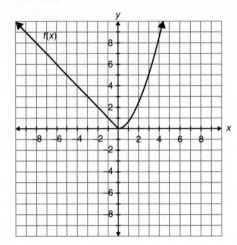

Problem 2 Reflecting

1. Graph each linear function on the grid shown.

   a. $f(x) = x + 5$

   b. $g(x) = -x + 5$

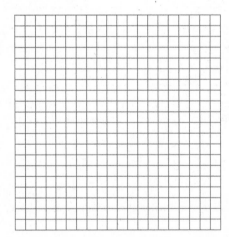

2. Evaluate the functions for each value.

    a. $f(2) =$ $g(-2) =$

    b. $f(-2) =$ $g(2) =$

    c. $f(5) =$ $g(-5) =$

    d. $f(-5) =$ $g(5) =$

3. Graph each square root function on the grid shown.

    a. $f(x) = \sqrt{x}$

    b. $g(x) = \sqrt{-x}$

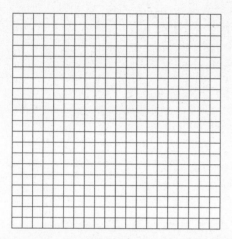

4. Evaluate the functions for each value.

    a. $f(1) =$ $g(-1) =$

    b. $f(4) =$ $g(-4) =$

    c. $f(9) =$ $g(-9) =$

    d. $f(16) =$ $g(-16) =$

5. Graph each cubic function on the grid shown.

   a. $f(x) = x^3$

   b. $g(x) = (-x)^3 = -x^3$

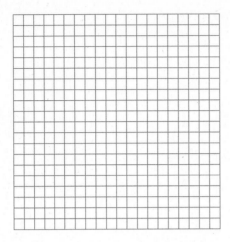

6. Evaluate the functions for each value.

   a. $f(1) =$ $\qquad$ $g(-1) =$

   b. $f(2) =$ $\qquad$ $g(-2) =$

   c. $f(-3) =$ $\qquad$ $g(3) =$

   d. $f(-2) =$ $\qquad$ $g(2) =$

7. In Questions 1, 3, and 5, can you write $g(x)$ in terms of $f(x)$? Explain.

8. In Questions 1, 3, and 5, what do you notice about the graphs of $f(x)$ and $g(x)$?

9. If the ordered pair (x, y) is on the graph of $f(x)$, then what point must be on the graph of $f(-x)$?

A **reflection** of a graph is the mirror image of the graph about a line. The line that the graph is reflected about is the **line of reflection.**

10. What is the line of reflection for the graphs in Questions 1, 3, and 5?

Problem 3 More Reflecting

1. Graph each linear function on the grid shown.

   a. $f(x) = x + 5$

   b. $g(x) = -x - 5$

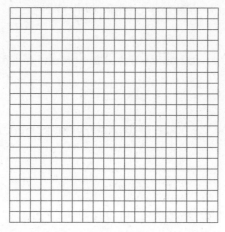

2. Evaluate the functions for each value.

   a. $f(2) =$ $g(2) =$

   b. $f(-2) =$ $g(-2) =$

   c. $f(5) =$ $g(5) =$

   d. $f(-5) =$ $g(-5) =$

3. Graph each square root function on the grid shown.

   a. $f(x) = \sqrt{x}$

   b. $g(x) = -\sqrt{x}$

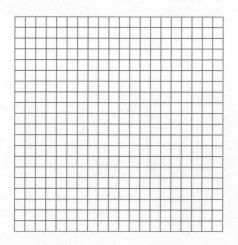

4. Evaluate the functions for each value.

   a. $f(1) =$ $g(1) =$

   b. $f(4) =$ $g(4) =$

   c. $f(9) =$ $g(9) =$

   d. $f(16) =$ $g(16) =$

5. In Questions 1 and 3, can you write $g(x)$ in terms of $f(x)$? Explain.

6. In Questions 1 and 3, what do you notice about the graphs of $f(x)$ and $g(x)$?

7. If the ordered pair (x, y) is on the graph of $f(x)$, then what point must be on the graph of $f(-x)$?

8. What is the line of reflection for the graphs in Questions 1 and 3?

Problem 4   Reflecting Twice

1. Graph the following square root functions using technology.

   a. $f(x) = \sqrt{x}$

   b. $g(x) = -\sqrt{-x}$

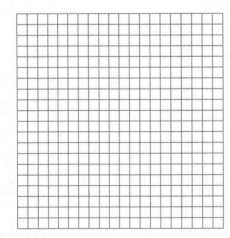

2. Evaluate the functions for each value.

    a. $f(1) =$ $g(-1) =$

    b. $f(4) =$ $g(-4) =$

    c. $f(9) =$ $g(-9) =$

    d. $f(16) =$ $g(-16) =$

3. Can you write $g(x)$ in terms of $f(x)$? Explain.

4. What do you notice about the graphs of $f(x)$ and $g(x)$?

5. If the ordered pair (x, y) is on the graph of $f(x)$, then what point must be on the graph of $g(x)$?

6. The graph of $f(x)$ is shown. Sketch the graph of

    a. $g(x) = f(-x)$

    b. $h(x) = -f(x)$

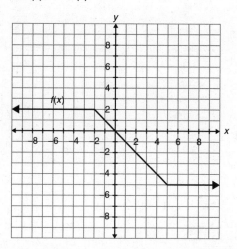

 Be prepared to share your methods and solutions.

9.3 Mirroring!
Symmetry and Odd/Even

Objectives

In this lesson, you will:

- Describe the symmetry of functions.
- Classify functions as odd and even.

Key Terms

- even function
- odd function

Problem 1 Symmetry

1. Graph each quadratic function on the grid shown.

   a. $f(x) = x^2$

   b. $g(x) = x^2 - 6x + 8$

   c. $h(x) = x^2 + 6x + 8$

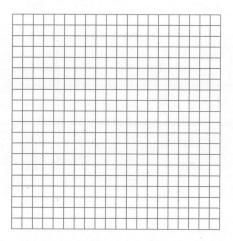

2. For each function in Question 1, identify the vertex, y-intercept, x-intercept(s), and line of symmetry.

Function	Vertex	y-Intercept	x-Intercept(s)	Line of Symmetry
$f(x) = x^2$				
$g(x) = x^2 - 6x + 8$				
$h(x) = x^2 + 6x + 8$				

3. Graph each absolute value function on the grid shown.

a. $f(x) = |x|$

b. $g(x) = |x + 2| - 3$

c. $h(x) = |x - 5| + 3$

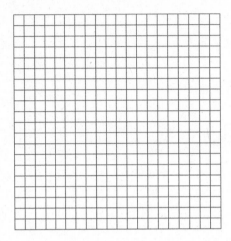

4. For each function in Question 3, identify the vertex, y-intercept, x-intercept(s), and line of symmetry.

Function	Vertex	y-Intercept	x-Intercept(s)	Line of Symmetry
$f(x) = |x|$				
$g(x) = |x + 2| - 3$				
$h(x) = |x - 5| + 3$				

5. Graph each cubic function on the grid shown.

   a. $f(x) = x^3$

   b. $g(x) = x^3 - 1$

   c. $h(x) = x^3 - 4x$

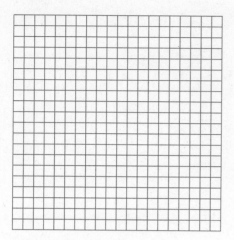

6. For each function in Question 5, identify the y-intercept, x-intercept(s), and line of symmetry.

Function	Vertex	y-Intercept	x-Intercept(s)	Line of Symmetry
$f(x) = x^3$				
$g(x) = x^3 - 1$				
$h(x) = x^3 - 4x$				

7. What do you notice about the vertex and the line of symmetry for each function in Questions 1 through 6?

8. What do you notice about the distance between the x-intercepts and the line of symmetry for each function in Questions 1–6?

9. Identify the equation of the line of symmetry, if it exists, for each graph shown.

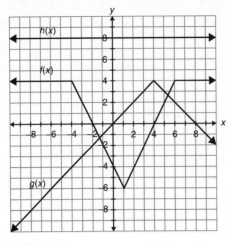

a. $f(x)$

b. $g(x)$

c. $h(x)$

10. Describe the result of reflecting a symmetric graph about its line of symmetry.

Problem 2 Odd and Even Functions

1. Graph each function on the grid shown.

   a. $f(x) = x^2$

   b. $g(x) = x^3 - 4x$

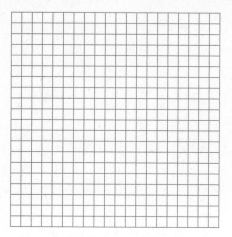

2. Graph each function on the grid shown.

   a. $h(x) = x^4 - 5x^2 + 4$

   b. $k(x) = x^5 - 5x^3 + 4x$

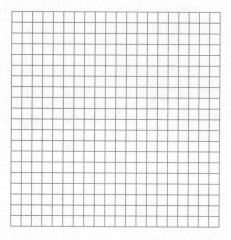

3. Which functions in Questions 1 and 2 are symmetric about the *y*-axis?

4. Describe the result of reflecting the graphs of the functions from Question 3 about the y-axis.

5. Evaluate the functions used in Questions 1 and 2 for each value.

a. $f(1) =$

$f(-1) =$

b. $f(4) =$

$f(-4) =$

c. $f(6) =$

$f(-6) =$

d. $f(x) =$

$f(-x) =$

e. $h(1) =$

$h(-1) =$

f. $h(2) =$

$h(-2) =$

g. $h(5) =$

$h(-5) =$

h. $h(x) =$

$h(-x) =$

6. If a function is symmetric about the y-axis, what is true about $f(x)$ and $f(-x)$?

An **even function** is a function such that $f(x) = f(-x)$ for all values of x. Even functions are symmetric with respect to the y-axis.

7. Describe the result of reflecting the graphs of $g(x)$ and $k(x)$ about the y-axis and then about the x-axis.

8. Evaluate the functions used in Questions 1 and 2 for each value.

    a. $g(1) =$

       $g(-1) =$

    b. $g(3) =$

       $g(-3) =$

    c. $g(2) =$

       $g(-2) =$

    d. $g(x) =$

       $g(-x) =$

    e. $k(1) =$

       $k(-1) =$

    f. $k(3) =$

       $h(-3) =$

    g. $k(2) =$

       $k(-2) =$

    h. $k(x) =$

       $k(-x) =$

9. What do you notice about $g(x)$ and $g(-x)$? About $k(x)$ and $k(-x)$?

An **odd function** is a function such that $f(x) = -f(-x)$ for all values of x.

10. Classify each function in Questions 1 and 2 as even or odd.

11. The portion of the graph of $f(x)$ to the right of the y-axis is shown. Sketch the portion of the graph to the left of the x-axis if

a. The function is an even function.

b. The function is an odd function.

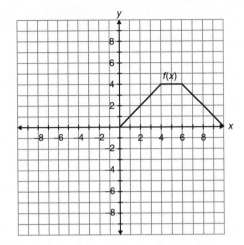

 Be prepared to share your methods and solutions.

9.4 Machine Parts
Solving Equations Graphically

Objective

In this lesson, you will:

- Solve equations algebraically and graphically.

Key Terms

- point of intersection
- consistent
- inconsistent
- identity

9

Problem 1 Machine Parts

A company sells a machine part for $15 with a fixed shipping charge of $25 for any number of parts. Another company sells the same part for $16 with a shipping charge of $1.50 per part.

1. Define variables for the independent and dependent quantities. Then write equations for the total cost of an order from each company.

2. Graph the equations from Question 1 on the grid shown.

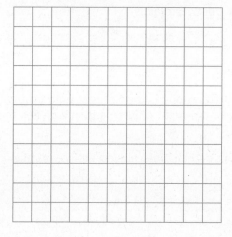

3. Does it make sense to connect the points of each graph? Explain.

4. Identify the slope and *y*-intercept for each function. What do the slope and *y*-intercept mean in terms of the problem?

5. An order consists of 10 machine parts. Calculate the cost from each company. Which company provides a lower total cost? Explain.

6. An order consists of less than 10 machine parts. Which company provides a lower total cost? Explain.

7. An order consists of more than 10 machine parts. Which company provides a lower total cost? Explain.

A **point of intersection** of two graphs is a point that both graphs have in common. The ordered pair of the point of intersection satisfies the equations representing the graphs.

The point of intersection can be calculated using tables, graphs, or equations.

8. Complete the table shown.

Number of Machine Parts	Cost from Company A	Cost from Company B
Parts		
x		
1		
2		
3		
4		
5		
6		
7		
8		
9		
10		
11		
12		
13		
14		
15		

9. Use the table of values to determine the point of intersection. How is the intersection point shown in the table?

10. Can you always use a table to determine a point of intersection? Explain.

11. Use the graph from Question 2 to determine the point of intersection. How is the intersection point shown on the graph?

12. Can you always use a graph to determine a point of intersection? Explain.

13. Use the equations to solve for the point of intersection algebraically.

14. Can you always use the equations to determine a point of intersection? Explain.

Problem 2   Solving Equations Graphically

The methods that you used in Problem 1 to determine the point of intersection can also be used to solve a single equation. To solve a single equation, define a function equal to the left side of the equation and a function equal to the right side of the equation. The x-coordinate of the point of intersection is the solution to the equation.

1. Consider the quadratic equation $x^2 = 5x - 4$. Define the function $f(x)$ equal to the left side of the equation and $g(x)$ equal to the right side of the equation.

$f(x) = $ _____ $g(x) = $ _____

2. Use a table of values to determine the point(s) of intersection of $f(x)$ and $g(x)$. What is the solution to the equation $x^2 = 5x - 4$?

x		
0		
1		
2		
3		
4		
5		
6		
7		
8		
9		
10		
11		

3. Use a graph to determine the point(s) of intersection of $f(x)$ and $g(x)$. What is the solution to the equation $x^2 = 5x - 4$?

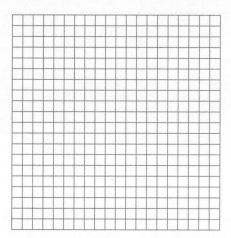

4. Compare the solutions using a table of values and the solutions using a graph. What do you notice?

5. Solve the quadratic equation $x^2 = 5x + 3$ using a table of values and a graph.

a. Define the function $f(x)$ equal to the left side of the equation and $g(x)$ equal to the right side of the equation.

$f(x) =$ $g(x) =$

b. Table of values:

x		
−2		
−1.5		
−1		
−0.5		
0		
0.5		
1		
1.5		
2		
2.5		
3		
3.5		
4		
4.5		
5		
5.5		
6		

c. Graph:

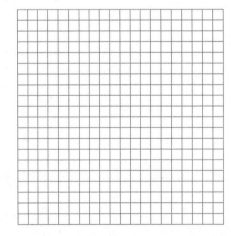

6. Did you determine exact solutions to $x^2 = 5x + 3$? Explain.

Two equations are **consistent** if the graphs of the two equations have at least one point of intersection. Two equations are **inconsistent** if the graphs of the two equations do not have a point of intersection.

7. Solve the cubic equation $x^3 + 2x^2 - x - 2 = (x + 1)(x - 1)(x + 2)$ using a graph.

   a. Define the function $f(x)$ equal to the left side of the equation and $g(x)$ equal to the right side of the equation.

      $f(x) =$ $g(x) =$

   b. Graph:

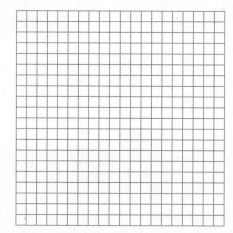

An **identity** is an equation that is true for all values of x. An identity has an infinite number of solutions. The graphs of the left and right sides of an identity are identical.

Problem 3 Solving Equations Graphically using Technology

In Problem 2 Question 5, you were not able to determine exact solutions to the equation $x^2 = 5x + 3$. Technology, such as a graphing calculator, can be useful to determine more accurate solutions.

1. Consider the quadratic equation $2^x = x^2 - 4$. Define the function $f(x)$ equal to the left side of the equation and $g(x)$ equal to the right side of the equation.

$f(x) = $ $g(x) = $

2. Graph $f(x)$ and $g(x)$ on the grid shown.

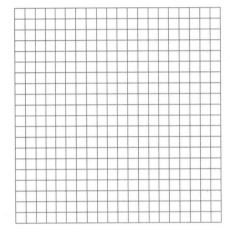

3. How many points of intersection exist?

4. Calculate an intersection point using a graphing calculator by performing the following.

   a. Press the Y= button. Enter the functions as Y_1 and Y_2.

   b. Graph the functions using appropriate bounds.

   c. Press the 2ND button and the TRACE button. You will see the CALC menu.

   d. Select 5: intersection.

   e. You will be prompted for the first function. Use the up and down buttons to toggle between functions. Select the first function.

   f. Use the left and right buttons to trace along the curve. Move the cursor to an intersection point and press ENTER.

g. You will be prompted for the second function. Use the up and down buttons to toggle between functions. Select the second function.

h. Use the left and right buttons to trace along the curve. Move the cursor to an intersection point and press ENTER.

i. You will be prompted for a guess. Use the left and right buttons to trace along the curve. Move the cursor close to an intersection point and press ENTER.

j. The coordinates of the intersection point will be displayed.

5. What is the point of intersection of $f(x)$ and $g(x)$? What is the solution to the equation $2^x = x^2 - 4$?

9

6. Solve the equation $x^2 - 6x + 8 = \sqrt{x}$ using a graphing calculator.

a. Define the function $f(x)$ equal to the left side of the equation and $g(x)$ equal to the right side of the equation.

$f(x) =$ $g(x) =$

b. Graph $f(x)$ and $g(x)$ on the grid shown.

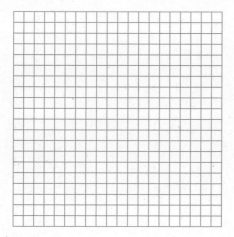

c. Solution(s):

 Be prepared to share your methods and solutions.

9

Bricks have been used as a building material for almost 10,000 years. Bricklayers, or masons, are skilled tradesmen who build structures by laying down bricks and binding them together with mortar. You will use rational equations and functions to calculate how quickly teams of bricklayers can construct building foundations.

© 2009 Carnegie Learning, Inc.

10.1 Roots and Zeros

Calculating Roots of Quadratic Equations and Zeros of Quadratic Functions

Objectives

In this lesson, you will:
- Solve quadratic equations.
- Calculate zeros of quadratic functions.

Key Terms

- Converse of the Multiplication Property of Zero
- roots
- zeros

Problem 1   Roots of Quadratic Equations

A quadratic expression of the form $x^2 + bx + c$ can be factored using an area model, a multiplication table, or the factors of the constant term c. The quadratic expression $x^2 - 4x - 5$ is factored using each method as shown.

- Area model

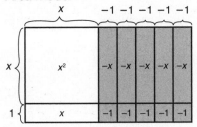

$x^2 - 4x - 5 = (x - 5)(x + 1)$

- Multiplication table

$\cdot$	x	-5
x	x^2	$-5x$
1	x	-5

$x^2 - 4x - 5 = (x - 5)(x + 1)$

- Factors of the constant term c

Factors of -5: $-5, 1$ $-1, 5$

Sums: $-5 + 1 = -4$ $5 + (-1) = 4$

$x^2 - 4x - 5 = (x - 5)(x + 1)$

The **Converse of the Multiplication Property of Zero** states that if the product of two or more factors is equal to zero, then at least one factor must be equal to zero.

If $ab = 0$ then $a = 0$ or $b = 0$.

1. Factor and solve each quadratic equation.

   a. $x^2 - 4x - 5 = 0$

   b. $x^2 - 8x + 12 = 0$

c. $x^2 - x - 6 = 0$

d. $x^2 - 5x - 24 = 0$

10

The solutions to quadratic equations are called **roots.**

2. Calculate the roots of each quadratic equation.

    a. $x^2 - 16 = 0$

    b. $x^2 - 5x + 6 = 0$

c. $x^2 - 5x - 36 = 0$

3. Factor and solve each quadratic equation, if possible.

a. $x^2 + 10x - 75 = 0$

b. $x^2 - 10x + 25 = 0$

c. $x^2 - 11x = 0$

Problem 2   Zeros of Quadratic Functions

1. Graph the quadratic function $f(x) = x^2 - 4x - 5$ on the grid shown.

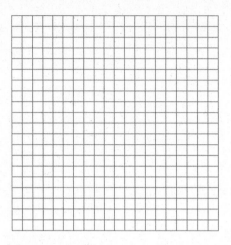

2. Identify the vertex, x- and y-intercepts, and line of symmetry. Label each on the grid.

   a. Vertex:

   b. y-intercept:

   c. x-intercept(s):

   d. Line of symmetry:

3. You calculated the roots of the quadratic equation $x^2 - 4x - 5 = 0$ in Problem 1 Question 1(a). What are the roots of $x^2 - 4x - 5 = 0$?

4. Compare the x-intercepts of the function $f(x) = x^2 - 4x - 5$ to the roots of the quadratic equation $x^2 - 4x - 5 = 0$. What do you notice?

5. The *x*-intercepts of a function are also called the **zeros** of the function. Why?

6. Calculate the zeros of each quadratic function, if possible.

  a. $f(x) = x^2 - 4x + 3$

  b. $f(x) = x^2 - 7x - 18$

  c. $f(x) = x^2 - 11x + 12$

d. $f(x) = x^2 + 10x - 39$

Be prepared to share your solutions and methods.

10.2 Poly High
Factoring Polynomials

Objectives
In this lesson, you will:
- Transform graphs of polynomial functions.
- Solve polynomial equations using factoring.

Key Terms
- polynomial equation
- greatest common factor
- factoring by grouping

Problem 1 Moving

The graph of the polynomial function $f(x)$ is shown on the grid.

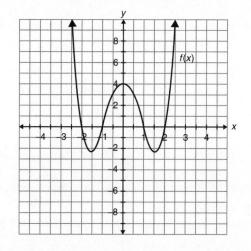

1. Identify the zeros, y-intercept, and line of symmetry for $f(x)$. Label each on the grid.

   a. Zeros:

   b. y-intercept:

   c. Line of symmetry:

2. Sketch the graph of each transformed function.

 a. $f(x) + 4$

 b. $f(x + 2)$

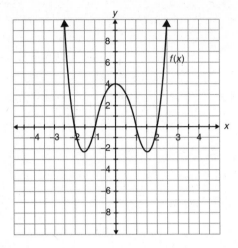

3. Describe how each graph is formed from the graph of $f(x)$.

 a. Five is subtracted from $f(x)$: $f(x) - 5$

 b. Four is subtracted from x: $f(x - 4)$

4. The graph of $f(x)$ is shown. Write a function in terms of $f(x)$ for the transformed graph.

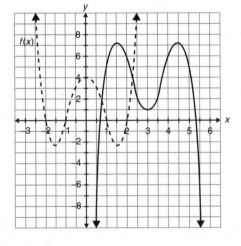

Problem 2   Solving Polynomial Equations

A **polynomial equation** is an equation that can be written in the form $a_n x^n + a_{n-1} x^{n-1} + a_{n-2} x^{n-2} + \ldots + a_2 x^2 + a_1 x + a_0 = 0$, where a is any real number and n is a positive integer. A linear equation is a first-degree polynomial equation because the highest power is 1. A quadratic equation is a second-degree polynomial equation because the highest power is 2.

The Converse of the Multiplication Property of Zero can be used to solve polynomial equations if the polynomial is factorable.

1. Factor and solve each polynomial equation.

    a. $x^2 - 5x + 4 = 0$

    b. $x^4 - 5x^2 + 4 = 0$

c. $x^4 - 8x^2 + 16 = 0$

d. $x^4 + 10x^2 + 9 = 0$

The **greatest common factor** of a polynomial is the largest factor that is common to all terms of the polynomial. Solving some polynomial equations requires factoring the greatest common factor and then factoring the remaining factor.

For example, solve the polynomial equation $2x^3 - 8x = 0$.

$2x^3 - 8x = 0$

Greatest common factor: $2x$

$2x(x^2 - 4) = 0$

$2x = 0$ or $x^2 - 4 = 0$

$x = 0$ or $(x - 2)(x + 2) = 0$

$x = 0$ or $x - 2 = 0$ or $x + 2 = 0$

$x = 0$ or $x = 2$ or $x = -2$

Check: $2(0)^3 - 8(0) = 0$

$2(2)^3 - 8(2) = 16 - 16 = 0$

$2(-2)^3 - e(-2) = -16 + 16 = 0$

2. Factor and solve each polynomial equation.

a. $4x^3 - 36x = 0$

b. $4x^3 - 4x^2 - 24x = 0$

c. $3x^3 - 27x^2 - 30x = 0$

Factoring by grouping is another method of factoring. To factor by grouping, create two groups of terms and factor the greatest common factor of each group. Then factor the greatest common factor of the groups.

For example, solve the polynomial equation $x^3 + 3x^2 - 4x - 12 = 0$.

$x^3 + 3x^2 - 4x - 12 = 0$

$x^2(x + 3) - 4(x + 3) = 0$

$(x^2 - 4)(x + 3) = 0$

$x^2 - 4 = 0$ or $x + 3 = 0$

$x - 2 = 0$ or $x + 2 = 0$ or $x = -3$

$x = 2$ or $x = -2$ or $x = -3$

Check: $(2)^3 + 3(2)^2 - 4(2) - 12 = 8 + 12 - 8 - 12 = 0$

$(-2)^3 + 3(-2)^2 - 4(-2) - 12 = -8 + 12 + 8 - 12 = 0$

$(-3)^3 + 3(-3)^2 - 4(-3) - 12 = -27 + 27 + 12 - 12 = 0$

3. Factor and solve each polynomial equation.

a. $x^3 + 4x^2 - 9x - 36 = 0$

b. $x^3 - 5x^2 + 3x - 15 = 0$

c. $2x^4 + 4x^3 - 2x^2 - 4x = 0$

 Be prepared to share your findings with the class.

10.3 Rational Thinking
Rational Equations and Functions

Objectives
In this lesson you will:
- Model situations with rational functions.
- Solve rational equations in one variable.

Key Terms
- rational equation
- extraneous solution

Problem 1

One day, Dan Petersen was having a disagreement with his father. During their discussion, Mr. Petersen said, "You should listen to me. I know more. I've lived longer. You're not even half my age." That got Dan thinking about when he would be half of his father's age. Right now, Dan is 16 years old and his father is 36 years old.

1. Calculate Dan's age as a percentage of his father's age.

2. How old was Dan's father when Dan was born?

3. When will Dan be half of his father's age? How old will each be?

4. When will Dan be three quarters of his father's age? How old will each be?

5. Will Dan ever be as old as his father? Explain.

6. If x represents Dan's age, what expression represents his father's age?

7. What expression represents the ratio of Dan's age to his father's age?

8. What are the domain and range for this problem situation?

9. What are the domain and range of the mathematical function, $f(x) = \dfrac{x}{x + 20}$?

10. Are your answers for Questions 8 and 9 the same? Explain.

11. Complete the following table of values.

x	$\dfrac{x}{x + 20}$
−70	
−60	
−50	
−40	
−30	
−20	
−10	
0	

x	$\dfrac{x}{x + 20}$
10	
15	
20	
30	
40	
50	
60	
70	

12. Create a graph using the values from the table.

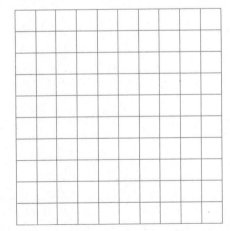

13. What are the *x*- and *y*-intercepts?

14. What are the intervals of increase and decrease?

15. Is the function continuous or discontinuous? If it is discontinuous, name any locations of discontinuity.

16. Describe the end behavior.

17. What are the asymptotes?

18. Explain why the function has the asymptotes it does. Your explanation may be in terms of either the mathematical function or of the problem situation.

19. Describe the behavior near the vertical asymptote.

20. Is the situation in this problem an example of direct variation, inverse variation, or neither? Explain your answer.

21. What type of function models this situation?

Problem 2

A **rational equation** is an equation containing one or more rational expressions. You have already solved simple rational equations with a single variable as a denominator.

1. Solve each of the following rational equations.

   a. $\dfrac{-3}{x} = -7$

   b. $\dfrac{5}{x} - 12 = 25$

   c. $\dfrac{5}{x} - 12 = \dfrac{25}{x}$

   d. $\dfrac{5}{x} = 25 + \dfrac{5}{x}$

   e. Does your solution check in part (d)? Explain

   f. When working with rational equations, you must limit your solution space based on the domain of the rational expressions. Explain.

In some rational equations, a rational expression is equal to a constant or to another rational expression. You can think of these equations as proportions. To solve them, you can cross multiply.

2. Solve each of the following rational equations. Make sure to list the restrictions to your solution set.

a. $\dfrac{12}{x + 5} = -2$

b. $\dfrac{7}{x + 3} = \dfrac{8}{x - 2}$

c. $\dfrac{x - 7}{x + 4} = -3$

d. $\dfrac{x - 5}{x - 2} = \dfrac{8}{9}$

e. $\dfrac{x^2 - 5x}{4} = \dfrac{8x}{2}$

f. $\dfrac{3x^3 - 5x}{3} = \dfrac{2x^3 - 10x + 4}{2}$

3. Solve the equation.

a. $\dfrac{5x}{6} - \dfrac{11}{12} + \dfrac{3x}{4} = \dfrac{2}{3}$

b. What was the first step in your solution path in part (a)? Why?

4. Using the same method, solve each of the following rational equations. Make sure to list the restrictions to your solution set.

    a. $\dfrac{-7}{x} + \dfrac{4}{7} - \dfrac{8}{x} = \dfrac{9}{7}$

    b. $\dfrac{3}{x+1} + \dfrac{2}{5x+5} = \dfrac{-3}{x+1}$

c. $\dfrac{3}{a-1} + \dfrac{2}{5a+5} = \dfrac{-3}{a^2-1}$

d. $\dfrac{3}{y} + \dfrac{-4}{5y} = -11$

5. Solve the rational equation.

a. $\dfrac{x+3}{x^2-1} + \dfrac{-2x}{x-1} = 1$

b. What happens when you check your answers?

c. While solving an equation, you sometimes multiply by a variable and increase the degree of the equation, thereby increasing the number of solutions. This is what happened in part (a). The extra solution is called an **extraneous solution.** In part (a), what is the actual solution, and what is the extraneous solution?

6. Solve each of the following rational equations. Make sure to identify any extraneous solutions, and make sure to list the restrictions to your solution set.

a. $\dfrac{3}{x + 1} - \dfrac{1}{x - 1} = \dfrac{2}{x^2 - 1}$

b. $\dfrac{-2}{x + 3} + \dfrac{3}{x - 2} = \dfrac{5}{x^2 + x - 6}$

c. $\dfrac{1}{x+2} + 1 = \dfrac{8}{x^2 - 2x - 8}$

d. $\dfrac{1}{x-5} = \dfrac{5}{x^2 + 2x - 35}$

10.4 Work, Mixture, and More
Applications of Rational Equations and Functions

Objectives

In this lesson, you will:
- Solve work problems.
- Solve mixture problems.
- Solve cost problems.

Key Terms

- work problems
- mixture problems
- cost problems

Problem 1   Work Problems

There is a class of problems that can be solved using rational equations and functions commonly called **work problems.**

1. Two teams of bricklayers are working on a new development of townhouses. Each quad of townhouses has the exact same block foundation. One team of bricklayers can complete this foundation in 30 hours, and the second team can complete it in 40 hours. If both teams work on the same foundation at once, how long will it take them to finish one set of quad townhouses? Complete parts (a) through (f) to answer this question.

   a. How much of the foundation will the first team of bricklayers complete in 10 hours? 20 hours? 1 hour? x hours?

   b. How long will it take the first team to finish $\frac{1}{2}$ of the job? $\frac{1}{5}$ of the job? $\frac{1}{30}$ of the job?

c. How much of the foundation will the second team of bricklayers complete in 10 hours? 20 hours? 1 hour? x hours?

d. How long will it take the second team to finish $\frac{1}{10}$ of the job? $\frac{1}{5}$ of the job? $\frac{1}{40}$ of the job?

e. If the two teams work together for x hours, write an expression that represents how much of the job they would complete.

f. Using the expression you wrote in part (e), write and solve an equation that represents one completed job. Then answer the following question: If both teams work on the same foundation at once, how long will it take them to finish one set of quad townhouses?

2. If Elaine is working alone, she can complete a job in 10 minutes. If she is working with José, the two of them can complete this job in 6 minutes. How long would it take José to complete this job if he is working alone? Complete parts (a) through (d) to answer this question.

a. Define a variable for the time it takes José to do the job alone.

b. Using the variable you defined in part (a), what fraction of the job can José complete in one minute?

c. What fraction of the job can Elaine complete in 6 minutes?

d. Write and solve an equation that represents one completed job when Elaine and José are working together. Use this equation to calculate the number of minutes it would take José to complete the job working alone.

Problem 2   Mixture Problems

Another class of problems using rational equations and functions is concentration, or **mixture problems.**

1. A saline or salt solution of 120 mL contains 10% salt. How much water would need to be added to this solution for it to contain only 2% salt? Complete parts (a) through (c) to answer this question.

    a. In the original saline solution, how many milliliters are there of salt? Of water? Explain how you know.

    b. What would the salt concentration of the solution be if you added 80 mL of water? 180 mL of water?

    c. Define a variable for the amount of water you need to add to the original solution. Use this variable to write and solve an equation to find how much water needs to be added to make the solution a 2% solution. Then answer the following question: How much water would need to be added to this solution for it to contain only 2% salt?

2. For the mixture described in Problem 2, define a function $C(x)$ for the concentration, where x is the amount of water added.

a. Using $C(x)$, graph the problem situation. Then identify the domain and range of the graph.

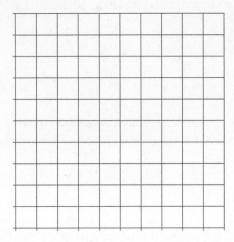

b. Now graph $C(x)$ as a mathematical function. Determine the domain, range, asymptotes, discontinuities, and end behavior of this function.

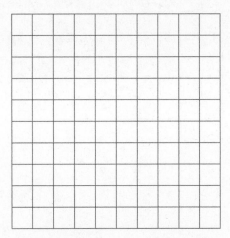

3. A 20% sulfuric acid 20 mL solution will be mixed with a 5% solution to produce other concentration solutions.

a. Will the new solution ever have a concentration of 20%? 5%? Explain.

b. If 20 mL of 20% solution is mixed with 10 mL of 5% solution, what will be the concentration of the resulting solution? Explain.

c. Define a variable for the amount of 5% solution added, and then define a function $S(x)$ for the concentration of the resulting solution.

d. Using $S(x)$, graph the problem situation. Then identify the domain and range of the graph.

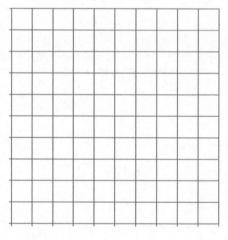

e. Now graph $S(x)$ as a mathematical function. Determine the domain, range, asymptotes, discontinuities, and end behavior of this function.

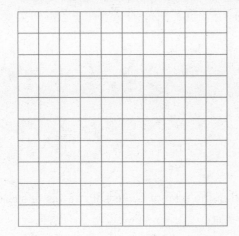

Problem 3   Cost of Ownership Problems

Another class of problems has to do with the total cost of owning something over time. These problems are called **cost problems.**

1. A new High Definition television costs $1600 and uses about $15 of electricity a year.

   a. Assuming that this television is reliable and its only costs of ownership are the original cost and the cost of electricity, what would be the average annual cost of owning this television after 5 years? 10 years?

© 2009 Carnegie Learning, Inc.

b. After how many years would the average annual cost be $115?

c. Determine the function of the cost of ownership of this television and define the variables.

d. Using $C(t)$, graph the problem situation. Then identify the domain and range of the graph.

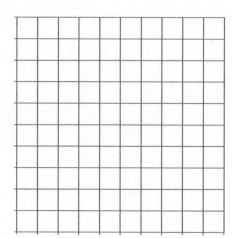

e. Now graph $C(t)$ as a mathematical function. Determine the domain, range, asymptotes, discontinuities, and end behavior of this function.

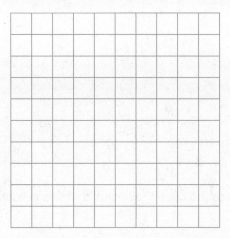

2. A new luxury automobile costs $75,000 to purchase, and it is estimated to cost about $8500 a year to own including fuel, service, repairs, and insurance.

   a. Assuming that these estimates are reliable and will not change, what would be the average annual cost of ownership after 5 years? 10 years?

b. After how many years would the average annual cost be $10,000?

c. Determine the function of the cost of ownership of this automobile and define the variables.

d. Using C(t), graph the problem situation. Then identify the domain and range of the graph.

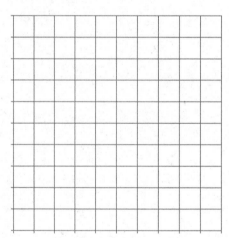

e. Now graph $C(t)$ as a mathematical function. Determine the domain, range, asymptotes, discontinuities, and end behavior of this function.

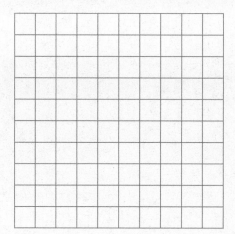

 Be prepared to share your work with another pair, group, or the entire class.

10

Objectives

In this lesson, you will:

● Transform graphs of radical functions.

● Solve equations involving radicals.

Problem 1   Moving

The graph of the basic radical function $f(x) = \sqrt{x}$ is shown on the grid.

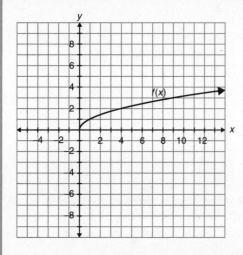

1. Identify the zeros and y-intercept of $f(x) = \sqrt{x}$. Label each point on the grid.

   a. Zeros:

   b. y-intercept:

2. Sketch the graph of each transformed function.

   a. $f(x) - 4$

   b. $f(x - 2)$

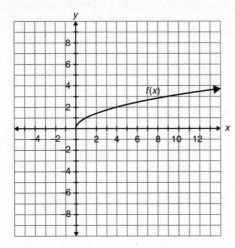

3. Describe how each graph is formed from the graph of $f(x)$.

   a. Five is added to $f(x)$: $f(x) + 5$

   b. Four is added to x: $f(x + 4)$

4. The graph of $f(x)$ is shown. Write a function in terms of $f(x)$ for the transformed graph.

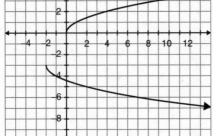

Problem 2

To solve an equation that contains a variable within a radical, you must first isolate the radical on one side of the equation. Once you have done this, remove the radical by raising both sides to the index of the radical.

For example: $\sqrt{2x} - 5 = 2$

$$\sqrt{2x} = 7$$
$$(\sqrt{2x})^2 = 7^2$$
$$2x = 49$$
$$x = \frac{49}{2}$$ Check: $\sqrt{2\left(\frac{49}{2}\right)} - 5 = 2$

1. Apply these steps to solve the following equation.

$$\sqrt{3x - 4} = 5$$

2. Solve each equation.

   a. $\sqrt{x} = 6$ **b.** $\sqrt{2x} = 3$

   c. $\sqrt[3]{2x - 3} = 2$ **d.** $4\sqrt{x - 6} = 8$

10

e. $\sqrt{2x + 1} = 5$ **f.** $2\sqrt[3]{x} + 16 = 0$

g. $\sqrt[4]{3x - 1} + 9 = 8$

Problem 3

In general, when solving for a variable in an equation that is raised to the nth power, you isolate the variable on one side of the equation and then take the nth root of each side (square root, cube root, fourth root, or other appropriate root).

In other words, to eliminate the nth power of the variable, you apply the *inverse operation*, which means taking the nth root of each side of the equation.

When solving any type of equation, you should always check to see whether the solution you obtain actually solves the original equation.

This is particularly important when you solve equations involving radicals because, in the process of solving the equation, apparent solutions may be introduced that do *not* solve the original equation. These apparent solutions are called extraneous solutions.

For example, whenever both sides of an equation are raised to a power, new solutions may be introduced that are not solutions to the original equation. Raising the degree of an equation increases the number of solutions.

Starting with $x = 2$, let's work backwards to an equation for this solution.

$x = 2$ Start with the original equation.

$x^2 = 4$ Square both sides of the equation.

$x^2 - 4 = 4 - 4$ Subtract 4 from each side.

$x^2 - 4 = 0$ Solve the resulting quadratic equation.

$(x - 2)(x + 2) = 0$

$x - 2 = 0$ or $x + 2 = 0$

$x = 2$ or $x = -2$

There are two solutions to the quadratic equation, but one ($x = -2$) is not a solution to the original equation. This extraneous solution results because the degree of the original equation is increased. The degree of the original equation is 1 (a linear equation). When you square each side of the equation, the degree is increased to 2 (a quadratic equation).

1. Solve each of the following and check for extraneous solutions or roots.

   a. $x - \sqrt{x} = 2$

   b. $x - 1 = \sqrt{x + 1}$

c. $-x + \sqrt[3]{3x^2 + 3x} = 1$

Be prepared to share your methods and solutions.

10.6 Connections
Algebraic and Graphical Connections

Objectives

In this lesson, you will:

- Describe transformations algebraically and graphically.
- Know the relationship between the zeros of a function and the roots of an equation.
- Solve equations algebraically and graphically.

Problem 1   Transformations

The graph of the basic absolute value function $f(x) = |x|$ and a transformed absolute value function $g(x)$ are shown on the grid.

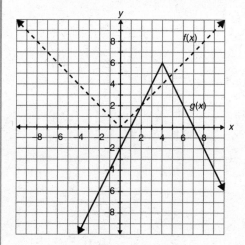

1. Identify each characteristic for $f(x)$.

   a. x-intercept(s):

   b. y-intercept(s):

   c. Vertex:

   d. Line of symmetry:

2. Identify each characteristic for $g(x)$.

   a. x-intercept(s):

   b. y-intercept(s):

   c. Vertex:

   d. Line of symmetry:

3. Describe how the graph of $g(x)$ is formed from the graph of $f(x)$ using four transformations.

4. Write a function in terms of $f(x)$ for $g(x)$.

5. Write a function for $g(x)$ using absolute value.

6. Is $f(x)$ an even function? An odd function? Explain.

7. Is $g(x)$ an even function? An odd function? Explain.

Problem 2   Roots and Zeros

1. Describe the relationship between the zeros of the function $f(x) = y$ and the roots of the equation $y = 0$.

2. Calculate the roots of the equation $x^3 - 4x^2 - 4x + 16 = 0$ algebraically.

3. Graph the function $f(x) = x^3 - 4x^2 - 4x + 16$ on the grid shown.

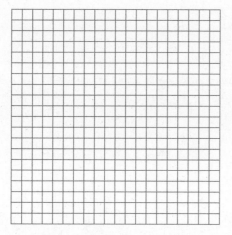

4. Identify the intercepts for $f(x)$.

   a. x-intercept(s):

   b. y-intercept(s):

5. What do you notice about the roots of the equation from Question 2 and the x-intercepts of the function from Question 4?

6. Calculate the roots of the equation $x^3 - 4x^2 - 4x = 0$ algebraically.

7. Graph the function $g(x) = x^3 - 4x^2 - 4x$ on the grid shown.

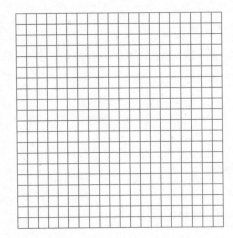

8. Identify the intercepts for $g(x)$.

   a. x-intercept(s):

   b. y-intercept(s):

9. Calculate the *x*-intercepts for $g(x) = x^3 - 4x^2 - 4x$ using a graphing calculator by performing the following.

   a. Press the Y= button. Enter the function as Y_1.

   b. Graph the function using appropriate bounds.

   c. Press the 2ND button and the TRACE button. You will see the CALC menu.

   d. Select 2: Zero.

   e. You will be prompted for the left bound. Use the left and right buttons to trace along the curve. Move the cursor to a point to the left of the *x*-intercept and press ENTER.

   f. You will be prompted for the right bound. Use the left and right buttons to trace along the curve. Move the cursor to a point to the right of the *x*-intercept and press ENTER.

   g. You will be prompted for a guess. Use the left and right buttons to trace along the curve. Move the cursor as close to the *x*-intercept as possible and press ENTER.

   h. The coordinates of the *x*-intercept will be displayed.

   i. Repeat steps (a) through (h) for each additional *x*-intercept.

Problem 3   Solving Equations Algebraically and Graphically

1. Solve each equation algebraically.

   a. $x^2 - 7x + 6 = 0$

b. $|x - 7| - 9 = 0$

c. $\sqrt{3x} - 6 = 0$

d. $2^x = 64$

e. $\dfrac{6x + 7}{x} = x$

2. Solve each equation graphically.

a. $\dfrac{x-2}{x} = x + 6$

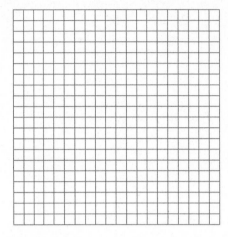

Solution(s):

b. $-x^2 + 6 = 2^x$

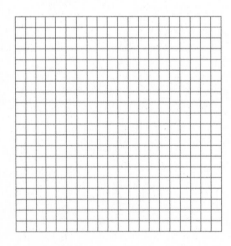

Solution(s):

c. $|x + 1| = x^2 - 5$

Solution(s):

Be prepared to share your methods and solutions.

The streets in many cities are organized using a grid system. In a grid system, the streets run parallel and perpendicular to one another, forming rectangular city blocks. You will use the Distance Formula to find the number of blocks between different locations in a city in which the streets are laid out in a grid system.

11.1 Meeting Friends
The Distance Formula

Objectives

In this lesson, you will:

- Determine the distance between two points.
- Use the Distance Formula.

Key Term

- Distance Formula

Two friends, Shawn and Tamara, live in a city in which the streets are laid out in a grid system.

Problem 1   Meeting at the Bookstore

Shawn lives on Descartes Avenue and Tamara lives on Elm Street as shown. The two friends often meet at the bookstore. Each grid square represents one city block.

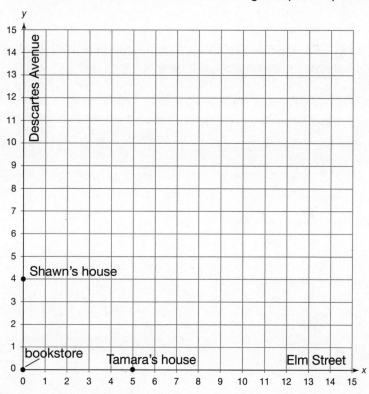

A. How far in blocks does Shawn walk to get to the bookstore?

4

B. How far in blocks does Tamara walk to get to the bookstore?

5

C. Tamara wants to meet Shawn at his house so that they can go to a baseball game together. Tamara can either walk from her house to the bookstore and then to Shawn's house, or she can walk directly to Shawn's house. Which distance is shorter? Explain your reasoning.

Directly because its a straight path

D. Determine the distance in blocks Tamara would walk if she traveled from her house to the bookstore and then to Shawn's house. Show all your work.

4 + 5 = 9 blocks

E. Determine the distance in blocks Tamara would walk if she traveled in a straight line from her house to Shawn's house. Show all your work. Round your answer to the nearest tenth of a block.

How did you calculate this distance?

Investigate Problem 1

1. Don, a friend of Shawn and Tamara, lives three blocks east of Descartes Avenue and five blocks north of Elm Street. Freda, another friend, lives seven blocks east of Descartes Avenue and two blocks north of Elm Street. Plot the location of Don's house and Freda's house on the grid. Label each location.

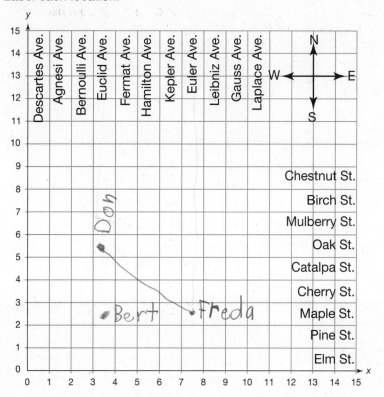

Name the streets that Don lives on.

Euclid ave. & Oak St.

Name the streets that Freda lives on.

Euler ave. & Maple St.

2. Another friend, Bert, lives at the intersection of the avenue that Don lives on and the street that Freda lives on. Plot the location of Bert's house on the grid in Question 1. Then describe the location of Bert's house with respect to Descartes Avenue and Elm Street.

2 blocks north of Elm St. and 3 blocks east of Descartes Ave.

3. Label the coordinates of the location of each house on the grid in Question 1. How do the coordinates of the location of Bert's house compare to the coordinates of the locations of Don's house and Freda's house?

Bert (4,3)

Don (4,6)

Freda (8,3)

Bert is a mix of Don's coordinates and Freda's coordinates.

4. Don and Bert often study French together. Use the house coordinates to write and evaluate an expression that represents the distance between Don's and Bert's houses.

How far in blocks does Don have to walk to get to Bert's house?

3 blocks

5. Bert and Freda often study chemistry together. Use the house coordinates to write an expression that represents the distance between Bert's and Freda's houses.

How far in blocks does Bert have to walk to get to Freda's house?

4 blocks

6. All three friends meet at Don's house to study geometry. Freda walks to Bert's house, and then they walk together to Don's house. Use the coordinates to write and evaluate an expression that represents the distance from Freda's house to Bert's house and from Bert's house to Don's house.

How far in blocks does Freda walk?

7 blocks

7. Draw the direct path from Don's house to Freda's house on the grid in Question 1. If Freda walks to Don's house on this path, how far in blocks does she walk? Explain how you determined your answer.

5 blocks

pythagorean theorem

8. Complete the summary of the steps that you took to determine the distance between Freda's house and Don's house. Let d be the direct distance between Don's house and Freda's house.

Distance between Bert's house and Freda's house		Distance between Don's house and Bert's house		Distance between Don's house and Freda's house
$(\square - \square)^2$	$+$	$(\square - \square)^2$		$= \square$
$\square^2$	$+$	$\square^2$		$= \square$
$\square$	$+$	$\square$		$= \square$
				$\square = \square$
				$\square = \square$

9. **Just the Math: The Distance Formula** You used the Pythagorean Theorem to calculate the distance between two points in the plane. Your method can be written as the *Distance Formula*.

Distance Formula

If (x_1, y_1) and (x_2, y_2) are two points in the coordinate plane, then the distance d between (x_1, y_1) and (x_2, y_2) is given by

$$d = \sqrt{(x_2 - x_1)^2 + (y_2 - y_1)^2}.$$

$=$ same as $a^2 + b^2 = c^2$

$c = \sqrt{(a_2 - a_1)^2 + (b_2 - b_1)^2}$

We indicate that distance is positive by using the absolute value symbol.

Do you think that it matters which point you identify as (x_1, y_1) and which point you identify as (x_2, y_2) when you use the Distance Formula? Explain your reasoning.

No because the distance between won't change

10. Calculate the distance between each pair of points. Round your answer to the nearest tenth if necessary. Show all your work.

a. (1, 2) and (3, 7)

5.4

b. (−6, 4) and (2, −8)

14.4

c. (−5, 2) and (−6, 10)

8.1

d. (−1, −2) and (−3, −7)

5.4

11. The distance between (*x*, 2) and (0, 6) is five units. Use the Distance Formula to determine the value of *x*. Show all your work.

 Be prepared to share your methods and solutions.

11

11.2 Treasure Hunt
The Midpoint Formula

Objective
In this lesson, you will:
- Use the Midpoint Formula.

Key Terms
- midpoint
- Midpoint Formula

A student teacher is designing a treasure hunt for the children in a kindergarten class. The goal of the treasure hunt is to have the children learn direction (right, left, forward, and backward) and start to learn about distance (near, far, in between). The treasure hunt will be on the school playground.

Problem 1   Plotting the Treasure Hunt

The student teacher has drawn a model of the playground on a grid as shown. The student teacher is using this model to decide where to place the items in the treasure hunt and to determine how to write the treasure hunt instructions. Each grid square represents a square that is one foot long and one foot wide.

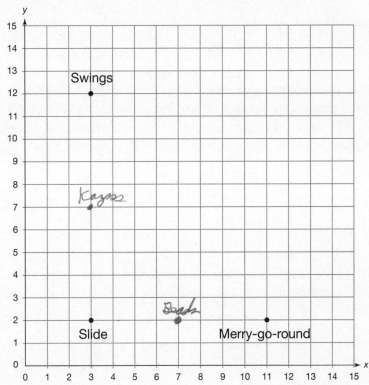

A. What are the coordinates of the merry-go-round, the slide, and the swings?

M ~ (11,2)
SL - (3,2)
SW - (3,12)

B. Determine the distance in feet between the merry-go-round and the slide. Show all your work.

8 feet

C. The teacher wants to place a small pile of beads in the grass halfway between the merry-go-round and the slide. How far in feet from the merry-go-round should the beads be placed? How far in feet from the slide should the beads be placed?

4 feet

4 feet

D. What should the coordinates of the pile of beads be? Explain how you determined your answer. Plot and label the pile of beads on the previous grid.

(7,2) That is halfway

How do the coordinates of the pile of beads compare to the coordinates of the slide and merry-go-round?

It is in the middle

E. The teacher also wants to place a pile of kazoos in the grass halfway between the slide and the swings. What should the coordinates of the pile of kazoos be? Show all your work and explain how you determined your answer. Plot and label the pile of kazoos on the grid on the previous page.

(3,7)

How do the coordinates of the pile of kazoos compare to the coordinates of the slide and swings?

It is halfway between both

Investigate Problem 1

1. The teacher wants to place a pile of buttons in the grass halfway between the swings and the merry-go-round. What do you think the coordinates of the pile of buttons will be? Explain your reasoning. Plot and label the pile of buttons on the following grid.

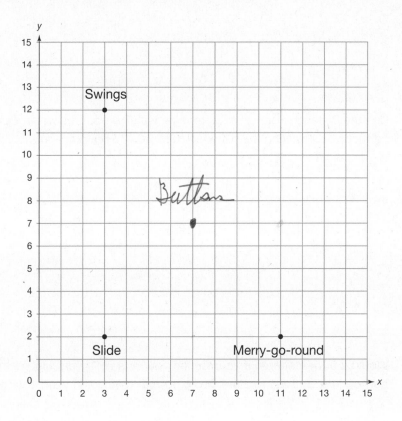

2. How far in feet from the swings and the merry-go-round will the pile of buttons be? Show all your work and explain how you determined your answer. Round your answer to the nearest tenth if necessary.

Use the Distance Formula to determine whether your answer in Question 1 is correct by calculating the distance between the buttons and the swings. Show all your work.

Would it have mattered if you verified your answer by calculating the distance between the buttons and the merry-go-round? Explain your reasoning.

3. Just the Math: Midpoint The coordinates of the points that you determined in part (D), part (E), and Question 1 are **midpoints,** or points that are exactly halfway between two given points. The work that you did in Problem 1 can be summarized in the *Midpoint Formula.*

Midpoint Formula

If (x_1, y_1) and (x_2, y_2) are two points in the coordinate plane, then the midpoint of the line segment that joins these two points is given by

$$\left(\frac{x_1 + x_2}{2}, \frac{y_1 + y_2}{2} \right).$$

Use the Midpoint Formula to verify your answer to Question 1.

4. Determine the midpoint of each line segment that has the given points as its endpoints. Show all your work.

a. (0, 5) and (4, 3)

$(2, 4)$

b. (8, 2) and (6, 0)

$(7, 1)$

c. (−3, 1) and (9, −7)

$(3, -3)$

d. (−10, 7) and (−4, −7)

$(-7, 0)$

Be prepared to share your methods and solutions.

11.3 Parking Lot Design
Parallel and Perpendicular Lines in the Coordinate Plane

Objectives

In this lesson, you will:

- Determine whether lines are parallel.
- Determine the equations of lines parallel to given lines.
- Determine whether lines are perpendicular.
- Determine the equations of lines perpendicular to given lines.
- Determine equations of horizontal and vertical lines.
- Calculate the distance between a line and a point not on the line.

Key Terms

- slope
- point-slope form
- slope-intercept form
- y-intercepts
- parallel lines
- perpendicular
- reciprocal
- negative reciprocal
- horizontal line
- vertical line

Large parking lots, such as those located in a shopping center or at a mall, have line segments painted to mark the locations where vehicles are supposed to park. The layout of these line segments must be considered carefully so that there is enough room for the vehicles to move and park in the lot without the vehicles being damaged.

Problem I Parking Spaces

Some line segments that form parking spaces in a parking lot are shown on the grid. One grid square represents a square that is one meter long and one meter wide.

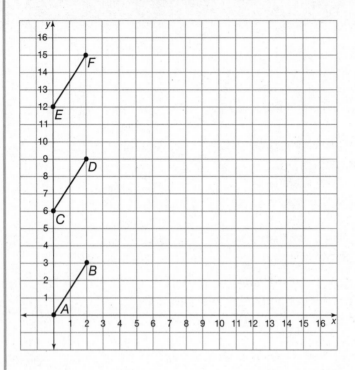

A. What do you notice about the line segments that form the parking spaces?

Take Note

Remember that the **slope** of a line is the ratio of the rise to the run:

slope = $\dfrac{\text{rise}}{\text{run}}$.

B. What is the vertical distance between $\overline{AB}$ and $\overline{CD}$ and between $\overline{CD}$ and $\overline{EF}$?

C. Carefully extend $\overline{AB}$ into line p, extend $\overline{CD}$ into line q, and extend $\overline{EF}$ into line r.

D. Use the graph to identify the slope of each line. What do you notice?

E. Use the point-slope form to write the equations of lines *p*, *q*, and *r*. Then write the equations in slope-intercept form.

What do you notice about the **y-intercepts** of these lines?

What do the y-intercepts tell you about the relationship between these lines?

F. If you were to draw a line segment above $\overline{EF}$ to form another parking space, what would be the equation of the line that coincides with this line segment? Determine your answer without graphing the line. Explain how you determined your answer.

Investigate Problem 1

1. What can you conclude about the slopes of **parallel lines** in the coordinate plane?

What can you conclude about the y-intercepts of parallel lines in the coordinate plane?

2. Write equations for three lines that are parallel to the line given by $y = -2x + 4$. Explain how you determined your answers.

3. Write an equation for the line that is parallel to the line given by $y = 5x + 3$ and passes through the point (4, 0). Show all your work and explain how you determined your answer.

4. Without graphing the equations, determine whether the lines given by $y - 2x = 5$ and $2x - y = 4$ are parallel. Show all your work.

Problem 2   More Parking Spaces

Another arrangement of line segments that form parking spaces in a truck parking lot is shown on the grid. One grid square represents a square that is one meter long and one meter wide.

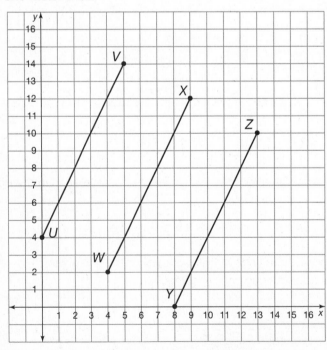

A. Use a protractor to determine the measures of ∠VUM, ∠XWY, and ∠ZYW. What similarity do you notice about the angles?

When lines or line segments intersect at right angles, we say that the lines or line segments are **perpendicular.** For instance, $\overline{UV}$ is perpendicular to $\overline{UW}$. In symbols, we can write this as $\overline{UV} \perp \overline{UW}$, where $\perp$ means "is perpendicular to."

B. Carefully extend $\overline{UY}$ into line p, extend $\overline{UV}$ into line q, extend $\overline{WX}$ into line r, and extend $\overline{YZ}$ into line s.

C. How do these lines relate to each other?

Complete each statement by using ‖ or $\perp$.

line p _____ line r

line q _____ line s

D. Without actually determining the slopes, how will the slopes of the lines compare? Explain your reasoning.

E. What do you think must be true about the signs of the slopes of two lines that are perpendicular?

F. Use the graph to determine the slopes of lines p, q, r, and s.

G. How does the slope of line p compare to the slopes of lines q, r, and s?

H. What is the product of the slopes of two of your perpendicular lines?

Investigate Problem 2

1. What can you conclude about the product of the slopes of perpendicular lines in the coordinate plane?

   When the product of two numbers is 1, the numbers are **reciprocals** of one another. When the product of two numbers is −1, the numbers are **negative reciprocals** of one another. So the slopes of perpendicular lines are negative reciprocals of each other.

2. Determine the negative reciprocal of each number.

   5   −2 $\dfrac{1}{3}$

3. Do you think that the *y*-intercepts of perpendicular lines tell you anything about the relationship between the perpendicular lines? Explain your reasoning.

4. Write equations for three lines that are perpendicular to the line given by $y = -2x + 4$. Explain how you determined your answers.

5. Write an equation for the line that is perpendicular to the line given by $y = 5x + 3$ and passes through the point (4, 0). Show all your work and explain how you determined your answer.

6. Without graphing the equations, determine whether the lines given by $y + 2x = 5$ and $2x - y = 4$ are perpendicular. Show all your work.

7. Complete each statement.

When two lines are parallel, their slopes are _____.

When two lines are perpendicular, their slopes are _____ _____.

8. Suppose that you have a line and you choose one point on the line. How many lines perpendicular to the given line can you draw through the given point?

9. Suppose that you have a line and you choose one point that is not on the line. How many lines can you draw through the given point that are perpendicular to the given line? How many lines can you draw through the given point that are parallel to the given line?

One final truck parking lot is shown. One grid square represents a square that is one meter long and one meter wide.

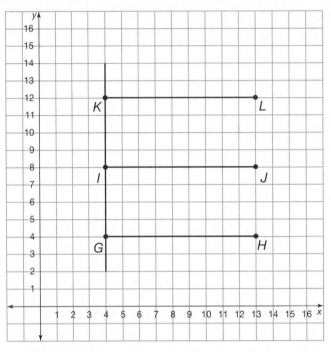

A. What type of angles are formed by the intersection of the parking lot line segments? How do you know?

B. Carefully extend $\overline{GK}$ into line p, extend $\overline{GH}$ into line q, extend $\overline{IJ}$ into line r, and extend $\overline{KL}$ into line s.

C. Choose any three points on line q and list their coordinates.

Choose any three points on line r and list their coordinates.

Choose any three points on line s and list their coordinates.

What do you notice about the x- and y-coordinates of these points?

© 2009 Carnegie Learning, Inc.

What do you think should be the equations of lines q, r, and s? Explain your reasoning.

D. Choose any three points on line p and list their coordinates.

What do you notice about the x- and y-coordinates of these points?

What do you think should be the equation of line p? Explain your reasoning.

Investigate Problem 3

1. **Just the Math: Horizontal and Vertical Lines** In Problem 3, you wrote the equations of horizontal and vertical lines. A **horizontal line** has an equation of the form $y = a$, where a is any real number. A **vertical line** has an equation of the form $x = b$, where b is any real number.

   Consider your horizontal lines in Problem 3. For any horizontal line, if x increases by one unit, by how many units does y change?

   What is the slope of any horizontal line? Explain your reasoning.

   Consider your vertical line in Problem 3. Suppose that y increases by one unit. By how many units does x change?

   What is the rise divided by the run? Does this make any sense? Explain.

   Because division by zero is undefined, we say that a vertical line has an undefined slope.

2. Consider the statements about parallel and perpendicular lines in Question 7 of Problem 2. Are these statements true for horizontal and vertical lines? Explain.

Complete the following statements.

_____ vertical lines are parallel.

_____ horizontal lines are parallel.

Write a statement that describes the relationship between a vertical line and a horizontal line.

3. Write equations for a horizontal line and a vertical line that pass through the point (2, −1).

4. Write an equation of the line that is perpendicular to the line given by $x = 5$ and passes through the point (1, 0).

Write an equation of the line that is perpendicular to the line given by $y = -2$ and passes through the point (5, 6).

Problem 4   Distances Between Lines and Points

1. Sketch a line and a point not on the line. Describe the shortest distance between the point and the line.

2. The equation of the line shown in the grid is $f(x) = \frac{3}{2}x + 6$. Draw the shortest segment between the line and the point $A(0, 12)$. Label the point where the segment intersects $f(x)$ as point B.

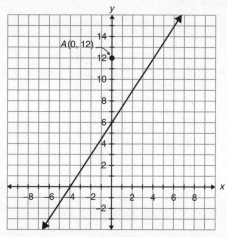

3. What information is needed to calculate the length of segment AB using the distance formula? Explain.

4. How can you calculate the intersection point of segment AB and the line $f(x) = \frac{3}{2}x + 6$ algebraically?

5. Write an equation for segment AB.

6. Calculate the point of intersection of segment AB and the line $f(x) = \dfrac{3}{2}x + 6$.

7. Calculate the length of segment AB.

8. What is the distance from the point $(0, 12)$ to the line $f(x) = \dfrac{3}{2}x + 6$?

9. Draw a line parallel to the line $f(x) = \dfrac{3}{2}x + 6$ that passes through the point $(0, 12)$. Identify another point on this parallel line.

10. Calculate the distance from the point in Question 9 to the line $f(x) = \dfrac{3}{2}x + 6$.

11. Compare your answers to Question 8 and Question 10. Is this a coincidence? Explain.

12. Calculate the distance from the origin to the line $f(x) = \frac{3}{2}x + 6$.

13. Predict the distance from the point (2, 3) to the line $f(x) = \frac{3}{2}x + 6$? Explain.

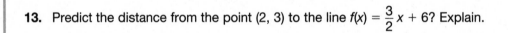

Be prepared to share your methods and solutions.

11.4 Building a Henge
Triangles in the Coordinate Plane

Objectives

In this lesson, you will:

- Study triangles inscribed in circles.
- Determine the relationship between the midpoint of the hypotenuse of a right triangle and the vertices of the triangle.
- Determine coordinates of midsegments of triangles.
- Discover properties of midsegments.
- Classify triangles in the coordinate plane.
- Construct an equilateral triangle.
- Construct points of concurrency.
- Solve for points of concurrency algebraically.

Key Terms

- inscribed triangle
- midsegment
- centroid
- points of concurrency
- circumcenter
- othocenter
- incenter
- equilateral triangle
- scalene triangle

11

In England, you can find flat, roughly circular areas of land that are enclosed by ditches, which are surrounded by piles of earth. These areas were created in ancient times and are called *henges*. The inner circular area of a henge can be accessed by entrances that were created through the surrounding ditches and piles of earth.

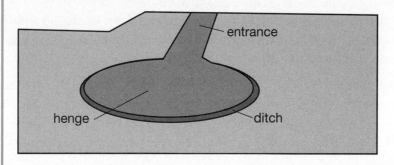

Problem 1   Build Your Own Henge

The circle on the coordinate plane represents the ditch of a henge. Each grid square represents a square that is three meters long and three meters wide. The points X, Y, and Z on this circle represent entrances to the inner area of the henge. Note that points X and Y are directly across the circle from one another.

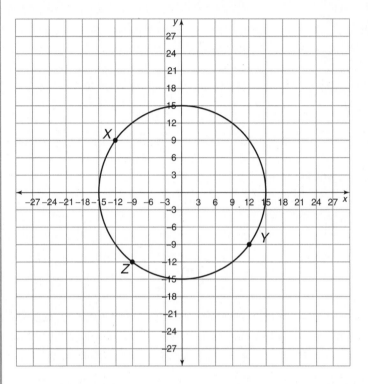

A. Choose three new points on the circle that will be the entrances to the inner area of the henge. Choose your points so that two of the points are the endpoints of a diameter. Label your points as points A, B, and C along with their coordinates on the coordinate plane.

B. Connect points A, B, and C with line segments to form a triangle. Your triangle is an *inscribed triangle*. An **inscribed triangle** is a triangle whose vertices lie on a circle.

C. Determine the slope of each side of your triangle. Show all your work.

D. Compare the slopes of the sides of the triangles. What do you notice?

E. Classify $\triangle ABC$ by its angles.

F. Repeat part (A) through part (E) for three different points. Name these points *D*, *E*, and *F*. Show all your work.

Investigate Problem 1

1. Write a conditional statement that describes the type of triangle that is created when the triangle is inscribed in a circle so that one side of the triangle is a diameter.

2. Consider a triangle inscribed in a circle so that one side of the triangle is a diameter. Classify the side that is the diameter. Is this true for every triangle that is constructed in this way? Explain your reasoning.

3. Can you draw an inscribed right triangle in which none of the sides are a diameter? If so, name the vertices of this triangle.

4. The circle on the coordinate plane presents the ditch of a different henge. Each grid square represents a square that is two meters long and two meters wide. Choose three points on the circle that will be entrances to the inner area of the henge so that the points form the vertices of a right triangle. Label your points as points *X, Y,* and *Z* along with their coordinates on the coordinate plane.

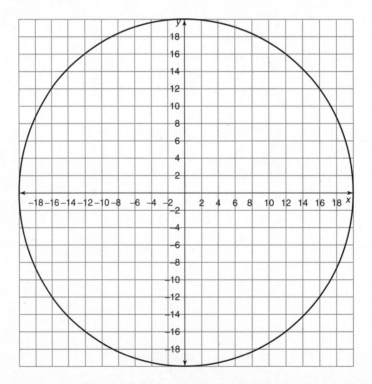

If (x_1, y_1) and (x_2, y_2), are two points in the coordinate plane, then the *midpoint* of the line segment that joins these two points is given by

$$\left(\frac{x_1 + x_2}{2}, \frac{y_1 + y_2}{2} \right).$$

Determine the coordinates of the midpoint of the hypotenuse. Label the midpoint on the graph as point *M*. Show all your work.

Calculate the distance from point *M* to each of the vertices of the right triangle. Show all your work. Simplify, but do not evaluate any radicals.

What do you notice?

5. Determine the midpoints of the other sides of your triangle in Question 4. Show all your work. Then label these midpoints on the graph as points *N* and *P* and connect all three midpoints with line segments. These line segments are the **midsegments** of the triangle.

Determine the slopes of the sides of your triangle in Question 4 and the slopes of the midsegments of the triangle. Show all your work.

What do you notice?

6. Determine the lengths of the sides of your triangle in Question 4 and the lengths of the midsegments. Show all your work. Simplify, but do not evaluate any radicals.

7. How does the length of a midsegment of a triangle compare to the length of the side of the triangle that the midsegment does not intersect? Show all your work.

Problem 2   Isosceles Triangles in the Coordinate Plane

1. The circle on the coordinate plane shown represents the ditch of a henge. Each grid square represents a square that is one meter long and one meter wide. The points (−6, −8), (6, −8), and (0, 10) represent entrances to the inner area of the henge. Label these three points.

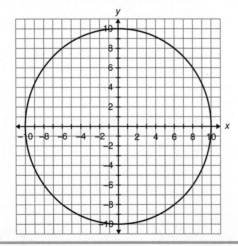

2. Form a triangle by connecting the three points. Classify the triangle based on the lengths of its sides.

3. How can you verify the classification from Question 2 using algebra?

4. Verify the classification from Question 2 using algebra.

Problem 3   Centroids in the Coordinate Plane

1. The **centroid** of a triangle is a **point of concurrency** formed by the intersection of the three medians of a triangle. How can you locate the centroid of the triangle from Problem 2 using geometric tools?

2. Use geometric tools to locate the centriod.

3. How can you locate the centroid of the triangle from Problem 2 using algebra?

4. Use algebra to locate the centroid.

5. Compare the coordinates of the centroid using geometric tools in Question 2 and algebra in Question 4.

Problem 4 Circumcenters in the Coordinate Plane

1. The **circumcenter** of a triangle is a point of concurrency formed by the intersection of the three perpendicular bisectors of a triangle. How can you locate the circumcenter of the triangle from Problem 2 using geometric tools?

2. Use geometric tools to locate the circumcenter.

3. How can you locate the circumcenter of the triangle from Problem 2 using algebra?

4. Use algebra to locate the circumcenter.

5. Compare the coordinates of the circumcenter using geometric tools in Question 2 and algebra in Question 4.

Problem 5   Points of Concurrency of Isosceles Triangles

1. Label the centroid and circumcenter of the triangle on the grid in Problem 2 Question 1.

2. The **orthocenter** of a triangle is a point of concurrency formed by the intersection of the three altitudes of a triangle. The **incenter** of a triangle is a point of concurrency formed by the intersection of the three angle bisectors of a triangle. Use geometric tools to locate the orthocenter and the incenter of the triangle from Problem 2. Label each on the grid. What do you notice about the four points of concurrency of an isosceles triangle?

11

Problem 6   Equilateral Triangles and Points of Concurrency

1. Construct an **equilateral triangle** on the grid shown by completing the following steps.

   a. Plot points $A(-10, -10)$ and $B(10, -10)$. Draw segment AB, one side of the equilateral triangle.

   b. Open the compass to a width equal to the distance between point A and point B.

   c. Place the point of the compass on point A. Draw an arc above segment AB.

   d. Keeping the compass at the same width. Place the point of the compass on point B. Draw an arc above segment AB.

   e. Label the intersection of the two arcs as point C. Draw segments AC and BC.

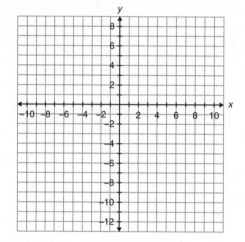

2. What are the coordinates of point C?

3. Construct the incenter, circumcenter, centroid, and othocenter. What do you notice about the four points of concurrency?

Problem 7   Scalene Triangles in the Coordinate Plane

1. Draw a large **scalene triangle** on the grid shown by plotting three points labeled *D*, *E*, and *F* and connecting the points.

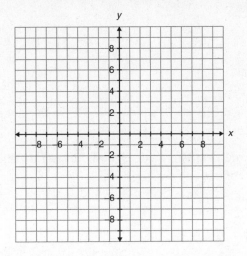

2. Identify the coordinates of the vertices of the scalene triangle.

3. Show that the triangle is scalene using geometric tools.

4. Show that the triangle is scalene using algebra.

5. Construct the incenter, circumcenter, centroid, and orthocenter of triangle *DEF*. Which of these points of concurrency are collinear?

Be prepared to share your methods and solutions.

11.5 Planning a Subdivision
Quadrilaterals in the Coordinate Plane

Objectives

In this lesson, you will:

- Classify quadrilaterals in the plane.
- Classify properties of quadrilaterals in the plane.

Key Terms

- rectangle
- parallelogram

A land planner is laying out different plots, or parcels, of land for a new housing subdivision. The parcels of land will be shaped like quadrilaterals.

Problem 1   The Lay of the Land

Parcel 1 is shown on the grid below. Each grid square has an area of one acre.

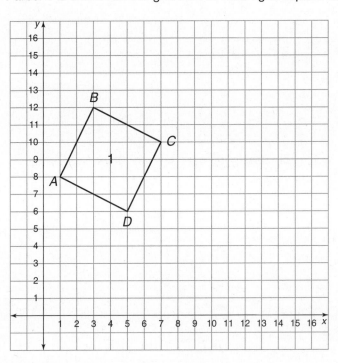

A. What kind of quadrilateral do you think parcel 1 is?

B. Find the slopes of each side of the parcel. How many pairs of opposite sides, if any, are parallel? Explain how you found your answer.

Are any of the sides perpendicular? Explain how you know.

Classify the quadrilateral with the information you have so far.

C. Find the lengths of the sides that form parcel 1. Show all your work. Are any of the side lengths congruent? If so, describe the sides that are congruent.

> ### Take Note
>
> Remember that the Distance Formula is
> $d = \sqrt{(x_2 - x_1)^2 + (y_2 - y_1)^2}$.
> You can use this formula to find the lengths of the sides that form parcel 1.

Can you classify parcel 1 further? If so, classify the quadrilateral.

Investigate Problem 1

1. The coordinates of the endpoints of parcel 2 are E(5, 1), F(5, 6), G(9, 6), and H(9, 1).
   Graph parcel 2 on the grid below. Classify this quadrilateral in as many ways as is
   possible. Explain how you found your answer.

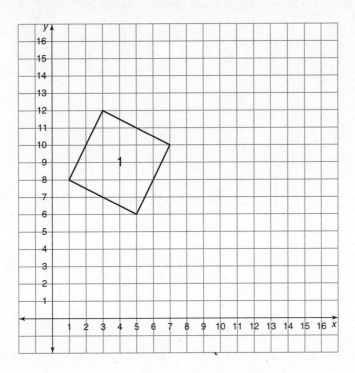

2. Should the diagonals of parcel 2 be congruent? Find the lengths of the diagonals
   to verify your answer.

3. The coordinates of the endpoints of parcel 3 are $I(5, 6)$, $J(7, 10)$, $K(11, 10)$, and $L(9, 6)$. Graph parcel 3 on the grid below. Classify this quadrilateral in as many ways as is possible. Explain how you found your answer.

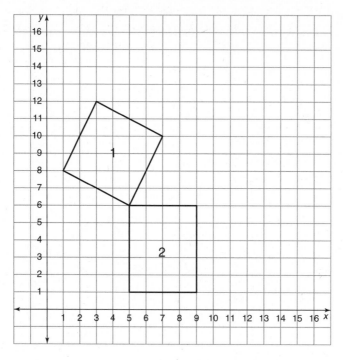

Problem 2

1. A land developer is creating parcels of land in the shape of parallelograms. Plot the points $Q(-3, -5)$, $R(2, -5)$, and $S(3, -3)$ on the grid shown.

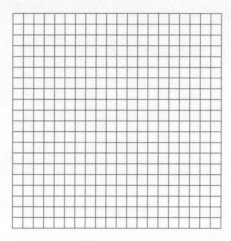

2. Locate a fourth point T such that the points Q, R, S, and T form a parallelogram. What are the coordinates of point T?

3. How can you verify that the quadrilateral is a parallelogram using algebra?

4. Use an algebraic strategy to verify the quadrilateral is a parallelogram.

5. Each square grid has an area of one acre. Calculate the area of the parcel of land defined by the parallelogram in Question 4.

6. Plot the points $Q(-3, -5)$, $R(2, -5)$, and $S(3, -3)$ on the grid shown.

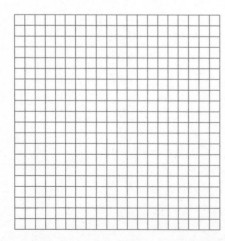

7. Locate a fourth point *T* that is different than the point in Question 2 and connect the four points to form a parallelogram. What are the coordinates of point *T*?

8. Use an algebraic strategy to verify the quadrilateral is a parallelogram.

9. Each square grid has an area of one acre. Calculate the area of the parcel of land defined by the parallelogram in Question 8. Remember that the height of the parallelogram is a perpendicular line segment that connects a vertex to the opposite side.

10. Did you calculate the same area in Questions 5 and 9? Why you think this result occurred?

11. Molly claims there is another possible location for point *T* such that the points *Q*, *R*, *S*, and *T* form a parallelogram. Is she correct? Explain.

 Be prepared to share your methods and solutions.

11

Glossary

absolute deviation

The absolute deviation is the absolute value of the difference between a data value and a measure of central tendency.

EXAMPLE

The mean score on a test is 82. Ruth scores a 97. The absolute deviation of Ruth's score to the mean is $|97 - 82| = |15| = 15$.

absolute value equation

An absolute value equation is an equation that includes one or more absolute value expressions.

EXAMPLE

The equation $|3x + 5| = 7$ is an absolute value equation.

acute triangle

An acute triangle is a triangle with three acute interior angles.

EXAMPLE

Angles A, B, and C are acute angles, so triangle ABC is an acute triangle.

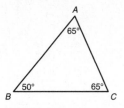

angle bisector

An angle bisector is a line, segment, or ray that divides an angle into two angles of equal measure.

EXAMPLE

Ray AT is the angle bisector of angle MAH.

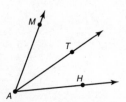

arithmetic sequence

An arithmetic sequence is a sequence in which the difference between any two consecutive terms is a constant called the common difference.

EXAMPLE

The sequence 1, 3, 5, 7 is an arithmetic sequence with a common difference of 2.

associative law

The associative law under addition states that $(a + b) + c = a + (b + c)$. The associative law under multiplication states that $a(bc) = (ab)c$.

EXAMPLE

$$(1 + 2) + 3 = 1 + (2 + 3)$$
$$3 + 3 = 1 + 5$$
$$6 = 6$$

average absolute deviation

The average absolute deviation is the average of the absolute deviation for each data value.

EXAMPLE

Samantha bowls 4 games and has scores of 130, 140, 150, and 180.

The mean bowling score is
$$\frac{130 + 140 + 150 + 180}{4} = \frac{600}{4} = 150.$$

The absolute deviations from the mean are $|130 - 150| = 20$, $|140 - 150| = 10$, $|150 - 150| = 0$, and $|180 - 150| = 30$.

The average absolute deviation is
$$\frac{20 + 10 + 0 + 30}{4} = \frac{60}{4} = 15.$$

average rate of change

The average rate of change is the ratio of the change in the dependent variable to the change in the independent variable. The average rate of change is calculated using the formula $\frac{y_2 - y_1}{x_2 - x_1}$.

EXAMPLE

The average rate of change between the points (1, 5) and (3, 9) is $\frac{9 - 5}{3 - 1} = \frac{4}{2} = 2$.

Glossary

base angle of an isosceles triangle

The base angles of an isosceles triangle are the angles that are opposite the equal sides.

EXAMPLE

Angles *A* and *B* are base angles of isosceles triangle *ABC*.

base of a geometric figure

The base of a geometric figure is the side or face to which an altitude is drawn, or is considered to be drawn.

EXAMPLE

Altitude *BD* is drawn to side *AC*, so side *AC* is the base of triangle *ABC*.

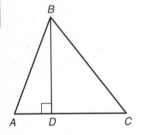

biconditional statement

A biconditional statement is the combination of a conditional statement and its converse using "If and only if."

EXAMPLE

Conditional statement: "If a quadrilateral has 4 right angles, then the quadrilateral is a rectangle."

Converse: "If a quadrilateral is a rectangle, then the quadrilateral has four right angles."

Both the conditional statement and its converse are true so they can be rewritten as the biconditional statement "A quadrilateral has four right angles if and only if the quadrilateral is a rectangle."

binomial

A binomial is a polynomial with exactly two terms.

EXAMPLE

The polynomial 3*x* + 5 is a binomial.

bisect an angle

To bisect an angle is to divide the angle into two smaller angles of equal measure.

EXAMPLE

Ray *BD* bisects angle *ABC* so $m\angle ABD = m\angle DBC$.

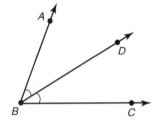

bisect a line segment

To bisect a line segment is to divide a line segment into two smaller segments of equal length.

EXAMPLE

Line segment *AB* has been bisected.

centroid

The centroid of a triangle is the point at which the medians of the triangle intersect.

EXAMPLE

Point *X* is the centroid of triangle *ABC*.

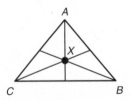

circular permutation

A circular permutation is an arrangement of objects in a circle.

EXAMPLE

The different ways in which 5 people can be seated around a circular table is a circular permutation.

circumcenter

The circumcenter of a triangle is the point at which the perpendicular bisectors intersect.

EXAMPLE

Point X is the circumcenter of triangle ABC.

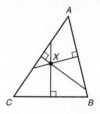

common difference

The common difference of an arithmetic sequence is a constant that represents the difference between any two consecutive terms.

EXAMPLE

The sequence 1, 3, 5, 7 is an arithmetic sequence with a common difference of 2.

common ratio

The common ratio of a geometric sequence is a constant that represents the ratio of any two consecutive terms.

EXAMPLE

The sequence 2, 4, 8, 16 is a geometric sequence with a common ratio of 2.

commutative law

The commutative law under addition states that $a + b = b + a$. The commutative law under multiplication states $ab = ba$.

EXAMPLE

Both $35 + 43$ and $43 + 35$ are equal to 78.

Both $6 \cdot 24$ and $24 \cdot 6$ are equal to 144.

compound events

A compound event is an event that is made up of two or more simple events.

EXAMPLE

Choosing two socks from a drawer is a compound event.

conclusion

Conditional statements are made up of two parts. The conclusion is the result that follows from the given information.

EXAMPLE

In the conditional statement "If two positive numbers are added, then the sum is positive," the conclusion is "the sum is positive."

concurrent lines

Concurrent lines are three or more lines that intersect at the same point.

EXAMPLE

Lines l, m, and n are concurrent lines.

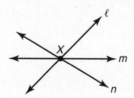

conditional probability

Conditional probability is the probability of event B happening, given that event A has already occurred.

The conditional probability is calculated as

$P(B \mid A) = \dfrac{P(A \cap B)}{P(A)}$, where $P(A \cap B)$ is the probability that both events occur and $P(A)$ is the probability of event A occurring.

EXAMPLE

Calculate the probability of rolling a total of 8 or more if the first roll of a standard number cube is a 5.

$$P(B \mid A) = \dfrac{P(A \cap B)}{P(A)} = \dfrac{\frac{1}{6} \cdot \frac{2}{3}}{\frac{1}{6}} = \dfrac{2}{3}$$

Glossary

conditional statement

Conditional statements are made up of two parts: the hypothesis and the conclusion.

EXAMPLE

The statement "If two positive numbers are added, then the sum is positive" is a conditional statement.

consecutive angles

Consecutive angles of a polygon are two angles that share a common side.

EXAMPLE

In rectangle *FGHI*:

Angles *I* and *F* are consecutive angles.

Angles *F* and *G* are consecutive angles.

Angles *G* and *H* are consecutive angles.

Angles *H* and *I* are consecutive angles.

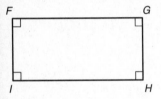

consecutive sides

Consecutive sides of a polygon are two sides that share a common vertex.

EXAMPLE

In the figure below:

Sides *IF* and *FG* are consecutive sides.

Sides *FG* and *GH* are consecutive sides.

Sides *GH* and *HI* are consecutive sides.

Sides *HI* and *IF* are consecutive sides.

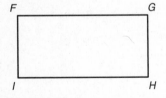

consistent

A system of equations that has at least one solution is consistent.

EXAMPLE
$$\begin{cases} y = -x - 2 \\ y = x - 2 \end{cases}$$
The system of equations is consistent.

contrapositive

The contrapositive of a conditional statement of the form "If *p*, then *q*" is the statement of the form "If not *q*, then not *p*." The contrapositive of a conditional statement may be true or false.

EXAMPLE

Consider the conditional statement "If a quadrilateral is a square, then the quadrilateral is a rectangle."

The contrapositive is "If a quadrilateral is not a rectangle, then the quadrilateral is not a square." The contrapositive is true.

converse

The converse of a conditional statement of the form "If *p*, then *q*" is the statement of the form "If *q*, then *p*." The converse of a conditional statement may be true or false.

EXAMPLE

Consider the conditional statement "If a quadrilateral is a square, then the quadrilateral is a rectangle."

The converse is "If a quadrilateral is a rectangle, then the quadrilateral is a square." The converse is false.

Converse of the Multiplication Property of Zero

The Converse of the Multiplication Property of Zero states that if the product of two or more factors is equal to zero, then at least one factor must be equal to zero.

EXAMPLE

If $(x + 2)(x - 3) = 0$ then $x + 2 = 0$ or $x - 3 = 0$.

Glossary

convex polygon

A convex polygon is a polygon in which no segments can be drawn to connect any two vertices so that the segment is outside the polygon.

EXAMPLE

The polygon on the left is a convex polygon.

The polygon on the right is not a convex polygon.

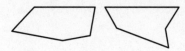

cost problems

A cost problem is a problem that involves the cost of ownership over time.

EXAMPLE

A problem that asks the average annual cost of owning a high definition TV over a five-year period is a cost problem.

counterexample

A counterexample is a specific example that shows that a conditional statement is false.

EXAMPLE

Consider the statement "The sum of two fractions is less than one."

A counterexample is $\frac{3}{4} + \frac{3}{4} = \frac{6}{4} = 1\frac{1}{2}$. The sum of the two fractions is greater than one so the original statement is false.

cubic function

A cubic function is a polynomial function with a degree of three.

EXAMPLE

The function $y = 2x^3 + 5x^2 - 7$ is a cubic function.

deductive reasoning

Deductive reasoning is reasoning that involves using a general rule to make a conclusion.

EXAMPLE

Sandy learned the rule that the sum of the measures of the three interior angles of a triangle is 180 degrees. When presented with a triangle, she concludes that the sum of the measures of the three interior angles is 180 degrees. Sandy reached the conclusion using deductive reasoning.

dependent events

Dependent events are events in which the outcome of one event affects the outcome of the other event.

EXAMPLE

Choosing a sock from a drawer, keeping the sock, and choosing another sock from the drawer are dependent events.

desired outcome

A desired outcome is an outcome of an event, which has a favorable result.

EXAMPLE

To calculate the probability of a coin landing heads up, the desired outcome is flipping the coin and having it land heads up.

diagonal

A diagonal is a line segment that connects any two non-adjacent vertices.

EXAMPLE

Segment FH is a diagonal of quadrilateral FGHI.

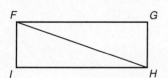

● dilation

A dilation is a transformation of a figure in which the figure stretches or shrinks with respect to a fixed point. The scale factor of a dilation is the ratio of a side length of the dilated figure to the original figure. An enlargement or reduction of a photo is an example of a dilation.

EXAMPLE

The original light hexagon is dilated to produce the dark hexagon by a scale factor of 2.

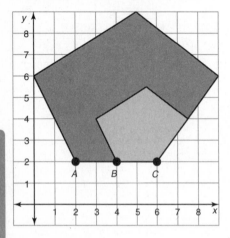

● direct argument

A direct argument is an argument that includes a conditional statement, a second statement formed by the hypothesis of the conditional statement, and a conclusion formed by the conclusion of the conditional statement.

EXAMPLE

Statement: If you do your math homework, then your teacher will be happy.

Statement: You did your math homework.

Conclusion: Therefore, your teacher is happy.

The conclusion was made using a direct argument.

● Distance Formula

The Distance Formula can be used to calculate the distance between two points.

The distance between points (x_1, y_1) and (x_2, y_2) is $d = \sqrt{(x_2 - x_1)^2 + (y_2 - y_1)^2}$.

EXAMPLE

To calculate the distance between the points $(-1, 4)$ and $(2, -5)$, substitute the coordinates into the Distance Formula.

$$d = \sqrt{(x_2 - x_1)^2 + (y_2 - y_1)^2}$$
$$d = \sqrt{(2 + 1)^2 + (-5 - 4)^2}$$
$$d = \sqrt{3^2 + (-9)^2}$$
$$d = \sqrt{9 + 81}$$
$$d = \sqrt{90}$$
$$d \approx 9.49$$

So, the distance between the points $(-1, 4)$ and $(2, -5)$ is approximately 9.49 units.

● distribution

A distribution is the way in which the data are distributed, such as being spread out or clustered together.

EXAMPLE

● distributive law

The distributive law states that for any numbers a, b, and c it is true that $a(b + c) = ab + ac$.

EXAMPLE

The distributive law can be used to write the expression $2(x + 4)$ as $2x + 8$.

● domain of a function

The domain of a function is the set of all input values for the function.

EXAMPLE

The domain of the function $y = 2x$ is the set of all real numbers.

equiangular triangle

An equiangular triangle is a triangle that has
all of its interior angles equal. The measure of
each interior triangle of an equiangular triangle is
60 degrees.

EXAMPLE

In triangle JKL, $m\angle 1 = m\angle 2 = m\angle 3 = 60°$. So,
triangle JKL is equiangular.

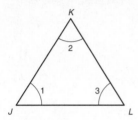

equilateral triangle

An equilateral triangle is a triangle that has all three
sides equal. The measure of each interior angle of
an equilateral triangle is 60 degrees.

EXAMPLE

Triangle ABC is an equilateral triangle, so
$m\angle 1 = 60°$, $m\angle 2 = 60°$, and $m\angle 3 = 60°$.

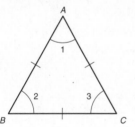

evaluating a function

Evaluating a function is the process of calculating
the value of a function for a specific value of the
independent variable.

EXAMPLE

Evaluate the function $f(x) = 2x + 4$ for $x = -2$.
$f(-2) = 2(-2) + 4 = -4 + 4 = 0$

even function

An even function f is a function for which
$f(-x) = f(x)$ for all values of x in the domain.

EXAMPLE

The function $f(x) = x^2$ is an even function because
$(-x)^2 = x^2$.

expected value

The expected value is the average value when the
number of trials is large.

EXAMPLE

You flip a coin and receive $1 if the coin lands
heads up and $2 if it lands tails up. The expected
value is $\frac{1}{2}(1) + \frac{1}{2}(2) = \frac{1}{2} + 1 = 1\frac{1}{2}$, or $1.50.

experimental probability

An experimental probability is a probability that is
based on repeated trials of an experiment.

EXAMPLE

You want to find the probability of a coin landing
heads up. You flip a coin 100 times and record
the results. The coin lands heads up 55 times and
lands tails up 45 times. The experimental
probability of the coin landing heads up is $\frac{55}{100}$.

explicit formula for a sequence

An explicit formula for a sequence is a rule for
calculating each term of the sequence using the
term's position in the sequence.

EXAMPLE

The sequence 1, 3, 5, 7, 9, ... can be described by
the rule $a_n = 2n - 1$, where n is the position of the
term. The fourth term of the sequence a_4 is
$2(4) - 1$, or 7.

exponent

An exponent indicates the number of times an
expression is multiplied by itself; that is, the
number of times the base is used as a factor.

EXAMPLE

In the expression 10^3, the number 3 is the
exponent. This indicates that the base 10 is used
as a factor 3 times: $10^3 = (10)(10)(10) = 1000$.

exponential function

An exponential function is a function of the form
$f(x) = a^x$, where $a > 0$ and $a \neq 1$.

EXAMPLE

The function $y = 2^x$ is an exponential function.

● exterior angle

An exterior angle of a polygon is an angle that is adjacent to an interior angle of a polygon.

EXAMPLE

Angle *JHI* is an exterior angle of quadrilateral *FGHI*.

Angle *EDA* is an exterior angle of quadrilateral *ABCD*.

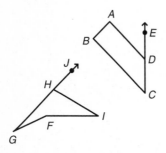

● Exterior Angle Inequality Theorem

The Exterior Angle Inequality Theorem states that the measure of an exterior angle of a triangle is greater than the measure of either of its remote interior angles.

EXAMPLE

By the Exterior Angle Inequality Theorem, the measure of angle 4 is greater than the measure of angle 1. It is also greater than the measure of angle 2.

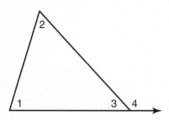

● extraneous solution

An extraneous solution is a solution that is introduced by multiplying by a variable increasing the degree of an equation. The extraneous solution is not a solution to the original equation.

EXAMPLE

Solve the rational equation

$$\frac{x + 3}{(x + 1)(x - 1)} + \frac{-2x}{x - 1} = 1$$

$x + 3 - 2x(x + 1) = (x + 1)(x - 1)$

$x + 3 - 2x^2 - 2x = x^2 - 1$

$3x^2 + x - 4 = 0$

$(3x + 4)(x - 1) = 0$

$3x + 4 = 0 \quad or \quad x - 1 = 0$

$x = -\frac{4}{3} \quad or \quad x = 1$

The solution $x = 1$ is an extraneous solution because it results in a denominator of zero when substituted into the original equation. So, the equation $\frac{x + 3}{(x + 1)(x - 1)} + \frac{-2x}{x - 1} = 1$ has one solution at $x = -\frac{4}{3}$.

● extrema

Extrema are the set of all relative maxima and minima for a graph.

EXAMPLE

The graph shown has 2 extrema, a relative maximum at (2, 3) and a relative minimum at (0, −1).

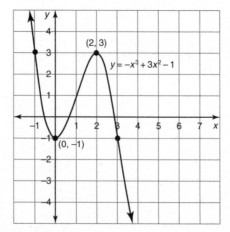

factoring a polynomial

Factoring is the process of expressing a polynomial as the product of monomials and binomials.

EXAMPLE

The polynomial $x^2 + 5x + 6$ can be written in factored form as $(x + 2)(x + 3)$.

factoring by grouping

Factoring by grouping is a method of factoring that involves creating two groups of terms. The greatest common factor of each group is factored and then the greatest common factor of the groups is factored.

EXAMPLE

Factor $x^3 + 3x^2 - 3x - 9$ using factoring by grouping.

$$x^3 + 3x^2 - 3x - 9 = x^2(x + 3) - 3(x + 3)$$
$$= (x + 3)(x^2 - 3)$$

finite sequence

A finite sequence is a sequence with a finite number of terms.

EXAMPLE

The sequence 2, 4, 6, 8, 10, 12 is a finite sequence.

function

A function is a relation in which there is exactly one output for every input.

EXAMPLE

The equation $y = 2x$ is a function. Every value of x has exactly one corresponding y-value.

functional notation

Functional notation is a notation used to write functions such that the dependent variable is replaced with the name of the function.

EXAMPLE

In the function $f(x) = 0.75x$, f is the name of the function, x represents the domain, and $f(x)$ represents the range.

general form of a quadratic trinomial

The general form of a quadratic trinomial is $ax^2 + bx + c$, where a, b, and c are constants and a is not equal to zero.

EXAMPLE

The quadratic trinomial $1 + 2x + x^2$ can be written in general form as $x^2 + 2x + 1$.

general term formula

See **explicit formula.**

geometric sequence

A geometric sequence is a sequence in which the ratio of any two consecutive terms is a constant called the common ratio.

EXAMPLE

The sequence 2, 4, 8, 16 is a geometric sequence with a common ratio of 2.

greatest common factor

The greatest common factor of two whole numbers is the largest whole number that is a factor of both numbers. The greatest common factor is abbreviated as GCF.

EXAMPLE

The whole number 3 is the greatest common factor of 6 and 9.

Glossary

horizontal line

A horizontal line has an equation of the form $y = a$, where a is any real number.

EXAMPLE

The equation $y = 2$ represents a horizontal line.

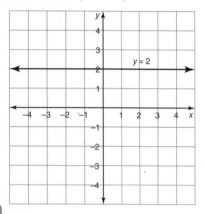

horizontal translation

A horizontal translation is a translation in which the preimage is moved either left or right to create the image.

EXAMPLE

Triangle ABC is translated horizontally 6 units to the left.

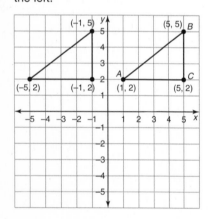

hypothesis

A hypothesis is the "If" part of an "If-then" statement.

EXAMPLE

In the statement, "If the last digit of a number is a 5, then the number is divisible by 5," the hypothesis is the part "If the last digit of a number is a 5."

identity

An identity is an equation that is true for all values of the variable. An identity has an infinite number of solutions.

EXAMPLE

The equation $2(x + 4) = 2x + 8$ is an identity.

identity law

The identity law for addition states that $a + 0 = a$. The identity law for multiplication states that $a \cdot 1 = a$.

EXAMPLE

$5 \cdot 1 = 5$

incenter

The incenter of a triangle is the point at which the angle bisectors of the triangle intersect.

EXAMPLE

Point X is the incenter of triangle ABC.

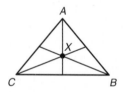

inconsistent

A system of equations that has no solution is inconsistent.

EXAMPLE

$\begin{cases} y = x + 5 \\ y = x - 2 \end{cases}$

The system of equations is inconsistent.

independent events

Independent events are two events in which the outcome of the first event does not affect the probability of the second event.

EXAMPLE

Choosing a sock from a drawer, replacing the sock, and choosing another sock from the drawer are independent events.

indirect argument

An indirect argument is an argument that is not direct.

EXAMPLE

Using a counterexample is one form of indirect argument.

indirect variation function

An indirect variation function is a function where the value of y varies indirectly to x. When x increase, y decreases proportionally and when x decreases, y increases proportionally.

EXAMPLE

The function $y = \frac{1}{x}$ is an indirect variation function.

inductive reasoning

Inductive reasoning is reasoning that involves using specific examples to make a conclusion.

EXAMPLE

Sandy draws several triangles, measures the interior angles, and calculates the sum of the measures of the three interior angles. She concludes that the sum of the measures of the three interior angles of a triangle is 180°. Sandy reached the conclusion using inductive reasoning.

inequality property

The inequality property states that if $a = b + c$ and $c > 0$, then $a > b$.

EXAMPLE

$7 = 5 + 2$ and $2 > 0$ so $7 > 5$

infinite sequence

A infinite sequence is a sequence with an infinite number of terms.

EXAMPLE

The sequence 2, 4, 6, 8, 10, 12, ... is an infinite sequence.

inscribed triangle

An inscribed triangle is a triangle whose vertices lie on a circle.

EXAMPLE

Triangle ABC is an inscribed triangle.

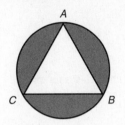

interior angle of a polygon

An interior angle of a polygon is an angle that faces the inside of a polygon and is formed by consecutive sides of the polygon.

EXAMPLE

The interior angles of $\triangle ABC$ are $\angle ABC$, $\angle BCA$, and $\angle CAB$.

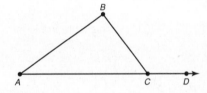

interval of decrease

An interval of decrease is a portion of a graph that is decreasing as you trace along the graph from left to right. An interval of decrease is described in terms of x-values.

EXAMPLE

The graph of $y = x^2 + 2$ is decreasing over the interval $(-\infty, 0)$.

interval of increase

An interval of increase is a portion of a graph that is increasing as you trace along the graph from left to right. An interval of increase is described in terms of x-values.

EXAMPLE

The graph of $y = x^2 + 2$ is increasing over the interval $(0, \infty)$.

Glossary

inverse law

The inverse law for addition states that
$a + (-a) = 0$. The inverse law for multiplication
states that $a \cdot \frac{1}{a} = 1$ for a not equal to zero.

EXAMPLE

$5 + (-5) = 0$

inverse of a function

The inverse of a one-to-one function is a function
that results from exchanging the independent and
dependent variables.

EXAMPLE

The inverse of a function $y = 2x$ is the function
$x = 2y$.

irrational number

An irrational number is a number that cannot be
written as $\frac{a}{b}$, where a and b are integers.

EXAMPLE

The numbers $\sqrt{2}$, 0.31311311..., and π are irrational
numbers.

isosceles trapezoid

An isosceles trapezoid is a trapezoid whose
non-parallel sides are congruent.

EXAMPLE

In trapezoid JKLM, side KL is parallel to side JM,
and the length of side JK is equal to the length
of side LM, so trapezoid JKLM is an isosceles
trapezoid. In trapezoid FGHI, side GH is parallel to
side FI, and the length of side FG is equal to the
length of side HI, so trapezoid FGHI is an isosceles
trapezoid.

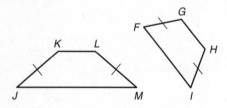

isosceles triangle

An isosceles triangle is a triangle with at least two
congruent sides.

EXAMPLE

Triangle ABC is an isosceles triangle.

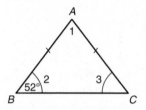

kite

A kite is a four-sided figure with two pairs of
adjacent sides of equal length.

EXAMPLE

In kite ABCD, sides AB and AD are the same length
and sides CB and CD are the same length.

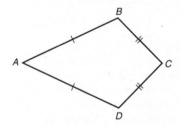

line of reflection

A line of reflection is a line in which a figure is
reflected.

EXAMPLE

The triangle is reflected in line k, so line k is a line
of reflection.

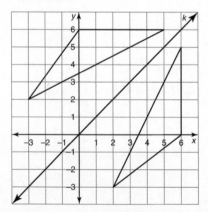

Glossary

line of symmetry

A line of symmetry is an imaginary line that divides a graph into two parts that are mirror images of each other.

EXAMPLE

Line K is the line of symmetry of the parabola.

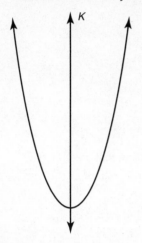

line symmetry

Line symmetry is a property of a graph such that a line can be drawn that divides the graph into two parts that are mirror images of one another. The line is called the line of symmetry.

EXAMPLE

The graph of $y = x^2$ displays the property of line symmetry.

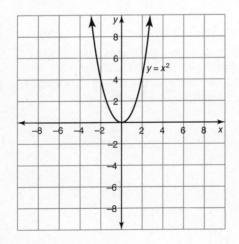

linear function

A linear function is a function whose graph is a non-vertical straight line.

EXAMPLE

$f(x) = 3x + 2$ is a linear function.

logically equivalent

Two propositional forms are logically equivalent if they have the same truth values for corresponding values of the propositional variables.

EXAMPLE

The conditional statement "If a number is even, then the number is divisible by two" is true. The statement's converse, inverse, and contrapositive are logically equivalent because they are all true as well.

mathematical sequence

A mathematical sequence, or just a sequence, is a number pattern or a list of numbers.

EXAMPLE

The list of numbers 1, 2, 4, 8, 16, 32, 64 is a mathematical sequence.

mean

The mean of a data set is the sum of all of the values of the data set divided by the number of values in the data set. The mean is also called the average.

EXAMPLE

The mean of the numbers 7, 9, 13, 4, and 7 is $\frac{7 + 9 + 13 + 4 + 7}{5}$, or 8.

measure of central tendency

A measure of central tendency is a single value that represents a typical value in a data set.

EXAMPLE

The mean, median, and mode are the most common measures of central tendency.

Glossary

median

The median of a data set that is arranged in numerical order is either the middle value (when the number of data values is odd), or the average of the two middle values (when the number of data values is even).

EXAMPLE

The median of the numbers 1, 5, 7, 10, 14 is 7.

median of a triangle

The median of a triangle is a segment drawn from a vertex to the midpoint of the opposite side.

EXAMPLE

The 3 medians are drawn on the triangle below.

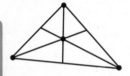

midpoint

The midpoint of a segment is the point that divides the segment into two congruent segments.

EXAMPLE

Because point B is the midpoint of segment AC, segment AB is congruent to segment BC.

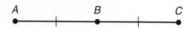

Midpoint Formula

The Midpoint Formula can be used to calculate the midpoint between two points. The midpoint between (x_1, y_1) and (x_2, y_2) is $\left(\dfrac{x_1 + x_2}{2}, \dfrac{y_1 + y_2}{2}\right)$.

To calculate the midpoint between the points $(-1, 4)$ and $(2, -5)$, substitute the coordinates into the Midpoint Formula.

$$\left(\frac{x_1 + x_2}{2}, \frac{y_1 + y_2}{2}\right) = \left(\frac{-1 + 2}{2}, \frac{4 - 5}{4} = \frac{1}{2}, \frac{-1}{2}\right)$$

So, the midpoint between the points $(-1, 4)$ and $(2, -5)$ is $\left(\dfrac{1}{2}, \dfrac{-1}{2}\right)$.

midsegments

A midsegment is a segment connecting the midpoints of two sides of a triangle.

EXAMPLE

Segment AB is a midsegment.

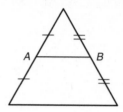

mixture problem

A mixture problem is a problem that involves the concentration of solutions.

EXAMPLE

A problem that asks the amount of water that is needed to dilute a 10% saline solution into a 7% saline solution is a mixture problem.

mode

The mode is the number (or numbers) that occurs most often in a data set. If there is no number that occurs most often, the data set has no mode.

EXAMPLE

The mode of the numbers 1, 3, 3, 5, 8, 10, 17 is 3.

monomial

A monomial is an expression that consists of a single term that is either a constant, a variable, or a product of a constant and one or more variables. A monomial is a polynomial with one term.

EXAMPLE

The expressions $5x$, 7, $-2xy$, and $13x^3$ are monomials.

negation of the conclusion

Negation of the conclusion is the initial step of a proof by contradiction, which assumes the opposite of the conclusion.

EXAMPLE

To prove the Triangle Exterior Angle Theorem using a proof by contradiction, begin by assuming that the measure of the exterior angle of a triangle is not equal to the sum of the measures of the two remote interior angles of the triangle.

negative reciprocal

The negative reciprocal of a rational number $\frac{a}{b}$ is $-\frac{b}{a}$. The product of a number and its negative reciprocal is -1.

EXAMPLE

The negative reciprocal of $\frac{2}{3}$ is $-\frac{3}{2}$.

obtuse triangle

An obtuse triangle is a triangle with one obtuse angle.

EXAMPLE

Angle B is an obtuse angle, so triangle ABC is an obtuse triangle.

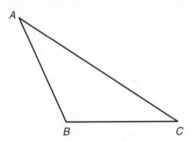

odd function

An odd function f is a function for which $f(-x) = -f(x)$ for all values of x in the domain.

EXAMPLE

The function $f(x) = x^3$ is an odd function because $(-x)^3 = -x^3$.

opposite angles

The opposite angles of a quadrilateral are two angles that do not share a common side.

EXAMPLE

In quadrilateral QRSP: Angle PQR and angle RSP are opposite angles. Angles QPS and QRS are opposite angles.

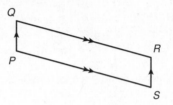

opposite sides

The opposite sides of a quadrilateral are two sides that do not intersect.

EXAMPLE

In quadrilateral QRSP, sides QR and PS are opposite sides. Sides QP and RS are opposite sides.

orthocenter

The orthocenter of a triangle is the point at which the altitudes of the triangle intersect.

EXAMPLE

Point X is the orthocenter of triangle ABC.

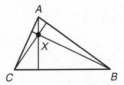

Glossary

outcomes

An outcome is a possible result of an event.

EXAMPLE

Flipping a coin has two outcomes: heads and tails.

outlier

An outlier is a data value that is much less or much greater than the other values in the data set.

EXAMPLE

The data set 1, 1, 3, 3, 4, 4, 5, 1000 has an outlier of 1000.

parallel lines

Two lines in the same plane are parallel to each other if they do not intersect.

EXAMPLE

Lines m and n are parallel.

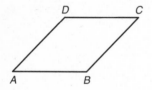

parallelogram

A parallelogram is a quadrilateral in which both pairs of opposite sides are parallel.

EXAMPLE

In parallelogram ABCD, opposite sides AB and CD are parallel; opposite sides AD and BC are parallel.

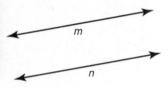

perfect square trinomial

A perfect square trinomial is a trinomial of the form $ax^2 + 2ab + b^2$ or $ax^2 - 2ab + b^2$. A perfect square trinomial can be written as the square of a binomial.

EXAMPLE

The trinomial $x^2 + 6x + 9$ is a perfect square trinomial because it is equal to the square of the binomial $x + 3$: $(x + 3)^2 = x^2 + 6x + 9$.

permutation with repeated elements

A permutation with repeated elements is a permutation of elements that contain one or more identical elements.

EXAMPLE

The number of three-letter strings that can be formed from the word NON is a permutation with repeated elements because the word NON has two Ns.

perpendicular bisector

A perpendicular bisector is a line, segment, or ray that intersects the midpoint of a line segment at a 90-degree angle.

EXAMPLE

Line k is the perpendicular bisector of segment AB. It is perpendicular to segment AB, and intersects segment AB at midpoint M so that AM = MB.

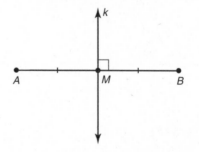

perpendicular

Two lines, segments, or rays are perpendicular if they intersect to form a right angle. The symbol for "is perpendicular to" is ⊥.

EXAMPLE

Lines m and k are perpendicular lines. Segment $AB \perp$ ray AC.

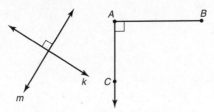

point of intersection

The point of intersection is the location on a graph where two lines or functions intersect, indicating that the values at that point are the same.

EXAMPLE

The point of intersection is the point (100, 300).

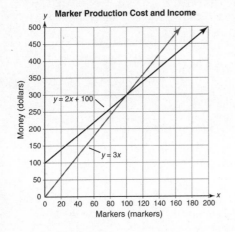

point-slope form of a linear equation

The point-slope form of a linear equation that passes through the point (x_1, y_1) and has slope m is $y - y_1 = m(x - x_1)$.

EXAMPLE

A line passing through the point (1, 2) with a slope of $\frac{1}{2}$ can be written in point-slope form as $y - 2 = \frac{1}{2}(x - 1)$.

point of concurrency

The point of concurrency is the point at which three or more lines intersect.

EXAMPLE

Point X is the point of concurrency for lines l, m, and n.

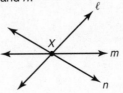

polynomial

A polynomial is an expression of the form $a_0 + a_1 x + a_2 x^2 + \ldots + a_n x^n$, where the coefficients $(a_0, a_1, a_2, \ldots)$ are real numbers or complex numbers and the exponents are non-negative integers.

EXAMPLE

The expression $3x^3 + 5x^2 - 6x + 1$ is a polynomial.

polynomial equation

A polynomial equation is an equation that can be written in the form $a_n x^n + a_{n-1} x^{n-1} + \ldots + a_2 x^2 + a_1 x + a_0 = 0$, where the coefficients are real numbers and n is a positive integer.

EXAMPLE

The equation $2x^3 - 4x + 1 = 0$ is a polynomial equation.

postulate

A postulate is a statement that is accepted to be true without proof.

EXAMPLE

The following statement is a postulate: "A straight line may be drawn between any two points."

Glossary

• probability

A probability is a number between 0 and 1 that is a measure of the likelihood that a given event will occur. The probability of an event when all outcomes are equally likely is equal to the number of desired outcomes divided by the number of possible outcomes.

EXAMPLE

The probability of rolling an even number with a six-sided number cube is $\frac{3}{6}$, or $\frac{1}{2}$.

• proof by contradiction

A proof by contradiction is a proof that assumes that the conclusion is false. The hypothesis is then proven to be false. So, the original conclusion must be true.

EXAMPLE

Use a proof by contradiction to prove the statement "If $a + bc = c(b + a) + a$ then $a = 0$ or $c = 0$."

Begin by assuming that both a and c are not equal to zero. So, let a and c both equal 2.

Steps	Reasons
$2 + 2b = 2(b + 2) + 2$	Assumption (negation of the conclusion)
$2 + 2b = 2b + 4 + 2$	Distributive law
$2 + 2b = 4 + 2 + 2b$	Commutative law of addition
$0 = 4$	Additive inverse

This is a contradiction to the original statement, which must be true.

• proof by contrapositive

A proof by contrapositive is a proof of the statement "If p, then q" using the argument "If not q, then not p."

EXAMPLE

Consider the statement "If having the most experience as a nuclear engineer had been the main requirement, then Olga would have gotten the job."

If you know that Olga did not get the job and can prove that having the most experience as a nuclear engineer was not the main requirement, then you have proven the original statement using a proof by contrapositive.

• propositional form

The propositional form of a conditional statement is the form "If p, then q."

EXAMPLE

The conditional statement "I always visit my grandmother on Sunday." can be written in propositional form as "If it is Sunday, then I will visit my grandmother."

• propositional variables

The propositional variables of a conditional statement "If p, then q" are the variables p and q.

EXAMPLE

Consider the conditional statement "If I eat, then I won't be hungry." The propositional variables are "I eat" and "I won't be hungry."

• quadratic function

A quadratic function is a function that can be written in the form $f(x) = ax^2 + bx + c$, where a, b, and c are real numbers and a is not equal to zero.

EXAMPLE

The equations $y = x^2 + 2x + 5$ and $y = -4x^2 - 7x + 1$ are quadratic functions.

• quadratic trinomial

A quadratic trinomial is a trinomial that has an exponent of 2 as the largest power of any term.

EXAMPLE

The trinomial $4x^2 - 5x + 1$ is a quadratic trinomial.

• radical symbol

The radical symbol ($\sqrt{}$) is the mathematical symbol used to indicate a square root.

EXAMPLE

The square root of 2 can be written using the radical symbol as $\sqrt{2}$.

Glossary

radicand

A radicand is the quantity under a radical sign in an expression.

EXAMPLE

In the expression $\sqrt[4]{25}$, the number 25 is the radicand.

random number

A random number is a number that is generated at random.

EXAMPLE

A graphing calculator has a RAND function that will generate a random number between 0 and 1.

random sample

A random sample is a sample that is created by selecting data values randomly.

EXAMPLE

A random sample of 5 students in a class can be created by writing each student's name on a piece of paper, placing the pieces of paper in a bag, and selecting 5 names.

range of a function

The range of a function is the set of all output values for the function.

EXAMPLE

The range of the function $y = x^2$ is the set of all numbers greater than or equal to zero.

rational equation

A rational equation is an equation that contains one or more rational expressions.

EXAMPLE

The equation $\dfrac{1}{x-1} + \dfrac{1}{x+1} = 4$ is a rational equation.

rational number

A rational number is a number that can be written in the form $\dfrac{a}{b}$, where a and b are both integers and b is not equal to 0.

EXAMPLE

The number -0.5 is a rational number because -0.5 can be written as $-\dfrac{1}{2} = \dfrac{-1}{2}$.

rationalizing the denominator

Rationalizing the denominator is a process of rewriting a radical expression so that the denominator does not contain a radical.

EXAMPLE

Rationalize the denominator of the expression $\dfrac{1}{\sqrt{2}}$.

$$\dfrac{1}{\sqrt{2}} = \dfrac{1}{\sqrt{2}} \cdot \dfrac{\sqrt{2}}{\sqrt{2}} = \dfrac{\sqrt{2}}{\sqrt{4}} = \dfrac{\sqrt{2}}{2}$$

reciprocals

Two non-zero numbers are reciprocals if their product is 1.

EXAMPLE

The fractions $\dfrac{2}{3}$ and $\dfrac{3}{2}$ are reciprocals.

rectangle

A rectangle is a parallelogram with four right angles.

EXAMPLE

Figure *ABCD*, figure *FGHI*, and figure *JKML* are rectangles.

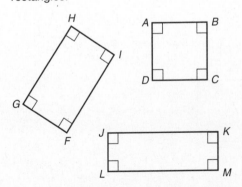

Glossary

• recursive formula for a sequence

A recursive formula for a sequence is a formula for defining all terms of a sequence in terms of the previous terms.

EXAMPLE

The sequence 10, 15, 20, 25, ... can be defined recursively as: $a_1 = 10, a_n = a_{n-1} + 5$

• reflection

A reflection is a transformation in which a figure is reflected, or flipped, in a given line called the line of reflection.

EXAMPLE

The triangle on the right is a reflection of the triangle on the left.

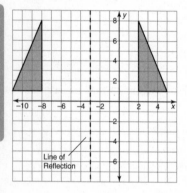

• regular polygon

A regular polygon is a polygon whose sides all have the same length and whose angles all have the same measure.

EXAMPLE

Figure *ABCD* and figure *EFG* are regular polygons.

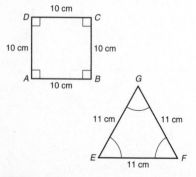

• regular tetrahedron

A regular tetrahedron is a four-sided solid with each face an equilateral triangle.

EXAMPLE

The solid shown is a regular tetrahedron.

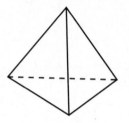

• relation

A relation is any set of ordered pairs.

EXAMPLE

The set of points {(0, 1), (1, 8), (2, 5), (3, 7)} is a relation.

• remote interior angles of a triangle

A remote interior angle of a triangle is an angle that is not adjacent to the referenced exterior angle.

EXAMPLE

Angle 1 and angle 2 are remote interior angles with respect to exterior angle 4.

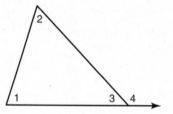

Glossary

rhombus

A rhombus is a parallelogram whose four sides have the same length. The plural form of "rhombus" is "rhombi."

EXAMPLE

Figure *JKLM* is a rhombus. Figure *ABCD* is a rhombus.

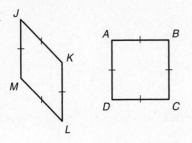

right triangle

A right triangle is a triangle that contains a right angle.

EXAMPLE

Triangle *ABC*, triangle *DEF*, and triangle *GHI* are right triangles.

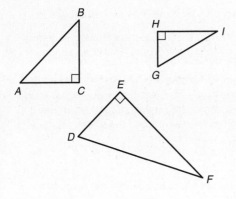

root of an equation

The root of an equation is the solution to the equation.

EXAMPLE

The equation $2x - 6 = 0$ has one root at $x = 3$.

sample

A sample is a group of items that are selected at random from a larger group of items called the population.

EXAMPLE

If the population of a study concerning health care includes everyone born in the United States from 1995 to 2005, then everyone born on May 22 of each year from 1995 to 2005 is a sample.

sample space

A sample space of a random experiment is the set of all possible outcomes of the experiment.

EXAMPLE

The sample space for flipping a coin twice consists of four outcomes: Heads-Heads, Heads-Tails, Tails-Heads, and Tails-Tails.

scalene triangle

A scalene triangle is a triangle with no sides of equal length.

EXAMPLE

None of the side lengths of triangle *ABC* are the same. So, triangle *ABC* is a scalene triangle. None of the side lengths of triangle *DEF* are the same. So, triangle *DEF* is a scalene triangle.

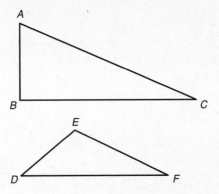

segment bisector

A segment bisector is a line, segment, or ray that divides a segment into two smaller segments of equal length.

EXAMPLE

Line segment *CD* is a segment bisector of segment *AB*. The length of segment *AE* is equal to the length of segment *BE*.

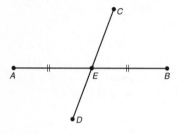

slope

The slope of a non-vertical line is the ratio of the vertical change to the horizontal change.

EXAMPLE

The slope of the line that passes through the points (3, −6) and (2, −4) is −2 because the vertical change is −2 units and the horizontal change is 1 unit.

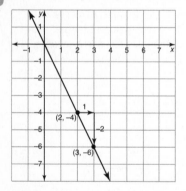

slope-intercept form of a linear equation

The slope-intercept form of a linear equation is $y = mx + b$, where m is the slope of the line and b is the *y*-intercept of the line.

EXAMPLE

The linear equation $y = 2x + 1$ is written in slope-intercept form. The slope of the line is 2 and the *y*-intercept is 1.

square

A square is a parallelogram with congruent sides and four right angles.

EXAMPLE

Figure *FGHI* and figure *ABCD* are squares.

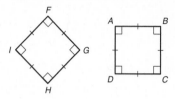

square root

A number *b* is a square root of *a* if $b^2 = a$.

EXAMPLE

The square roots of 25 are 5 and −5.

square root function

A square root function is a function in which the independent variable is contained within a square root.

EXAMPLE

The function $y = \sqrt{1.5x}$ is a square root function.

stem-and-leaf plot

A stem-and-leaf plot is a visual display of data that is organized by digits. Each data value is separated into a stem and a leaf. The leading digits of the data value are represented by the stem and the last digit is represented by the leaf.

EXAMPLE

A stem-and-leaf plot can be drawn to represent test scores.

55, 62, 73, 75, 76, 79, 80, 83, 86, 87, 87, 88, 88, 89, 89, 89

The tens' place represents the stem and the ones' place represents the leaves.

Stem-and-Leaf Plot of Test Scores

Stems	Leaves	Key: 7	3 = 73
1	
2	
3	
4	
5	5
6	2
7	3 5 6 9
8	0 3 6 7 7 8 8 9 9 9

Glossary

term of a sequence

A term is a member of a sequence. The first term is the first object or number in the sequence; the second term is the second object or number in the sequence; and so on.

EXAMPLE

In the sequence 2, 4, 6, 8, 10, the first term is 2, the second term is 4, and the third term is 6.

terms of an expression

The terms of an expression are the parts that are added together. A term may be a number, a variable, or a product of a number and a variable or variables.

EXAMPLE

The polynomial $2x + 3y + 5$ has three terms: $2x$, $3y$, and 5.

tessellation

A tessellation of a plane is a collection of polygons that are arranged so that they cover the plane with no holes or gaps.

EXAMPLE

The figures below are tessellations.

theorem

A theorem is a statement that has been proven to be true.

EXAMPLE

The Pythagorean Theorem states that if a right triangle has legs of lengths a and b and hypotenuse of length c, then $a^2 + b^2 = c^2$.

theoretical probability

A theoretical probability is a probability that is based on knowing all of the possible outcomes that are equally likely to occur.

EXAMPLE

The theoretical probability of a coin landing heads up is $\frac{1}{2}$.

trapezoid

A trapezoid is a quadrilateral with exactly one pair of parallel sides. The parallel sides are called bases and the non-parallel sides are called legs. The perpendicular distance between the bases is the height of the trapezoid.

EXAMPLE

Quadrilateral $ABCD$ is a trapezoid. The height is 4 meters, the length of base AD is 12 meters, and the length of base BC is 6 meters.

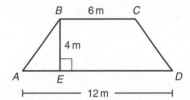

Triangle Exterior Angle Theorem

The Triangle Exterior Angle Theorem states that the measure of the exterior angle of a triangle is equal to the sum of the measures of the two remote interior angles of the triangle.

EXAMPLE

By the Triangle Exterior Angle Theorem, $m\angle 4 = m\angle 1 + m\angle 2$.

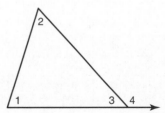

Glossary

trinomial

A trinomial is a polynomial that consists of three terms.

EXAMPLE

The polynomial $5x^2 - 6x + 9$ is a trinomial.

truth table

A truth table is a table that summarizes the possible truth values of a conditional statement.

EXAMPLE

p	q	$p \rightarrow q$
T	T	T
T	F	F
F	T	T
F	F	T

truth value

The truth value of a conditional statement is whether the statement is true or false.

EXAMPLE

The conditional statement "If two points are drawn, then there is one straight line that connects them" has a truth value of true.

two-column proof

A two-column proof is a proof consisting of two columns. In the left column are mathematical statements that are organized in logical steps. In the right column are the reasons for each mathematical statement.

EXAMPLE

The proof below is a two-column proof that angle 1 is congruent to angle 3.

Statement	Reason
1. Angle 1 and angle 3 are vertical angles	1. Given
2. Angle 1 and angle 2 form a linear pair. Angle 2 and angle 3 form a linear pair.	2. Definition of linear pair
3. Angle 1 and angle 2 are supplementary. Angle 2 and angle 3 are supplementary.	3. Linear Pair Postulate
4. Angle 1 is congruent to angle 3.	4. Congruent Supplements Theorem

Venn diagram

A Venn diagram uses circles to show how elements among sets of numbers or objects are related.

EXAMPLE

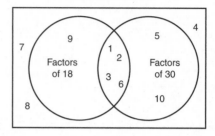

vertical line

A vertical line is a line of the form $x = a$, where a is a real number.

EXAMPLE

The line represented by the equation $x = 5$ is a vertical line.

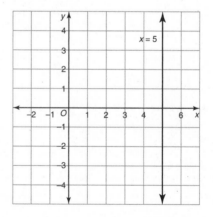

vertical motion model

A vertical motion model is an equation of the form $y = -16t^2 + vt + h$, where t is the time in seconds that the object has been moving, v is the initial velocity (speed) of the object in feet per second, h is initial height of the object in feet, and y is the height of the object in feet at time t seconds.

EXAMPLE

A rock is thrown in the air at a velocity of 10 feet per second from a cliff that is 100 feet. The height of the rock is modeled by the equation $y = -16t^2 + 10t + 100$.

● vertical translation

A vertical translation is a translation in which the preimage is moved either up or down to create the image.

EXAMPLE

Triangle *ABC* is translated vertically 7 units down.

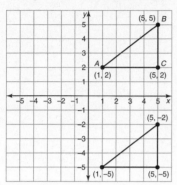

● with replacement

Two events with replacement is when an object is selected and then replaced before another item is selected.

EXAMPLE

Selecting a card, replacing the selected card in the deck, and selecting another card is two events with replacement.

● without replacement

Two events without replacement is when an object is selected and then not replaced before another item is selected.

EXAMPLE

Selecting a card, keeping the selected card out of the deck, and selecting another card is two events without replacement.

● work problems

A work problem is a problem that involves the rates of several workers and the time it takes to complete a job.

EXAMPLE

A problem that asks the time that it will take for two bricklayers working at different rates to complete a job is a work problem.

● x-intercept

The *x*-intercept is the *x*-coordinate of the point where a graph crosses the *x*-axis.

EXAMPLE

The *x*-intercept of the graph below is 4.

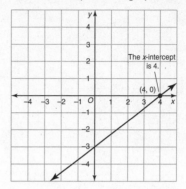

● y-intercept

The *y*-intercept is the *y*-coordinate of the point where a graph crosses the *y*-axis.

EXAMPLE

The *y*-intercept of the graph below is −3.

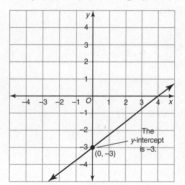

● zero of a function

The zero of a function $f(x)$ is an *x*-value such that $f(x) = 0$.

EXAMPLE

The linear equation $f(x) = 3x + 6$ has one zero at $x = -2$.

$$3x + 6 = 0$$
$$3x = -6$$
$$x = -2$$

Glossary

Index

Index

by SAS Congruence Theorem, 239–240

by SAS Similarity Postulate, 238–239

by SSS Congruence Theorem, 237–239

by SSS Similarity Postulate, 237–239

Consecutive angles, 269

Consecutive sides, 269

Consistent equations, 401

Contrapositive, 120–122

Converse, 116–118

Converse of the Multiplication Property of Zero, 408

Convex polygon, 281, 287, 290

Cost problems, solving, 441–445

Counterexample, 110–111, 122

Cubic functions, representing
    using equations, 36, 37
    using graphs, 35–37
    using tables, 35
    using words, 33–35

D

Data analysis, 339–368
    collecting and analyzing sample data, 365–368
    measures of central tendency, 341–346
    population and sample means, 359–363
    population data and samples, 347–358

Deductive reasoning, 103–106

Delta conyne kite, 266

Dependent events, probability of, 296

Desired outcomes of probability, 294

Diagonal
    defined, 263
    of hexagon forming triangles, 281

of isosceles trapezoid, 267

of kite, 263, 265, 277

of polygon, connecting single vertex, 282

of rectangle, 276–277

of rhombus, 272–273, 277

of square, 277

Diamond kite, 263–265

Dilation, 377–380

Direct argument, 109, 111, 112

Direct proof
    conditional statements proved by, 129–130
    theorems proved by, 228–229, 232

Distance Formula
    defined, 469
    using, 469–471

Distribution of data, 343

Distributive law, 131

Dodecagon, 282

Domain
    of algebraic functions, determining, 73–81
    defined, 5
    of relations, determining, 5, 8, 10, 12

E

Endpoints, 35

Equations
    algebraically solving, 395–398
    consistent/inconsistent, 401
    graphically solving, 398–401
        using technology, 402–403
    identity, 401
    involving radicals, solving, 449–452
    solving algebraically, 457–459
    solving graphically, 460–461

Equiangular triangles, 197–198

Equilateral triangles, 204–205, 504

Evaluating a function, 51

Even functions, 391–393

Expected value, 329–332

Experimental probability, 333–337

Explicit formula, 62

Exponents, 45

Exponential functions
    calculating, in average rate of change, 94–95
    representing
        using equations, 45, 46
        using graphs, 45–46, 47–48
        using tables, 47–48
        using words, 44–45

Exterior Angle Inequality Theorem
    defined, 202, 228
    proving, 202, 228–229

Exterior angles
    defined, 198–200, 287
    of polygons, 285–290
        defined, 287
        hexagons, 289
        measure of, determining, 288, 289–290
        sum of, determining, 288, 289–290
    of triangles, 198–200, 287
    See also Triangle Exterior Angle Theorem

Extraneous solution, 431–433

Extrema, 20

Extreme points, 20, 84–88

F

Factorial key, 315

Factorials, 315

Factoring
    by grouping, 420–422
    defined, 164
    polynomials, 415–422

Finite sequence, 59

Fractions involving factorials, simplifying, 315

Functional notation, 51–56

Functions

   analyzing problems using
      multiple representations,
      184–186, 189–191

   defined, 5

   evaluating, 51

   even, 391–393

   graphs of, interpreting, 30–31

   intervals of decrease for, 26

   intervals of increase for, 26

   modeling with, 181–191

   odd, 393–394

   relations as, 5, 8, 10, 12

   representing

      advantages/disadvantages
         of, 13

      using equations, 12, 27, 29,
         52–53

      using graphs, 4–6, 7–8,
         9–10, 11–12, 23–26,
         27–31, 55–56

      using tables, 3, 6, 9, 11, 27,
         30–31, 54–55

      using words, 10–11, 26

   sequence as, 60–62

   symmetry of, 387–390

   See also Average rate of
      change of functions

G

General form of a quadratic
   trinomial,
   167–168

General term formula, 62

Geometric sequence, 68–70

Graphing calculators

   factorial key on, 315

   permutations key on, 316

   solving equations with,
      402–403

Graphs

   dilation, 377–380

   extreme points of, calculating,
      84–88

line of reflection, 382, 384

lines of symmetry of,
   identifying, 85–88

point of intersection, 396–398

of polynomial functions,
   transforming,
   415–416

of radical functions,
   transforming, 447–448

reflection, 380–385

solving equations using,
   398–401, 398–403

transformations described
   using, 453–454

translations of

   horizontal, 374–376

   vertical, 371–373

x- and *y*-intercepts of,
   determining, 86–88

H

Hexagon

   exterior angle measures of,
      determining, 289

   identifying, 117, 119, 121, 279

   interior angle measures of,
      determining, 281, 289

   triangles formed by diagonals
      of, 281

Horizontal lines

   defined, 487

   determining, 487–488

   slope of, 487

Horizontal translation of a graph,
   374–376

Hypotenuse, 174, 496–497

Hypotenuse-Leg (HL)
   Congruence Theorem,
   249–253

Hypothesis, 109, 111–112

I

Identity, 401

Identity law, 131

Incenter, 214–215, 503

Inconsistent equations, 401

Independent events of
   probability, 296, 303

   See also Trials of independent
      events

Indirect argument, 110–111,
   112

Indirect proofs, 132–133

   irrational numbers proved by
      using, 178

   proof by contradiction,
      132–133

   theorems proved by using,
      227, 233

Indirect variation functions,
   38–40

Inductive reasoning, 103–106

Inequality property, 228

Infinite sequence, 59

Inscribed triangle, 494–496

Interior angles

   classifying triangles using
      measures of, 195–198,
      203–205

   defined, 280

   of hexagons, determining,
      281, 289

   measures, sum of, 280

   of polygons, determining,
      279–283

   remote, 199

Intervals of decrease, 26

Intervals of increase, 26

Inverse, 118–120

Inverse law, 131

Irrational numbers,
   178–179

Isosceles trapezoids

   base angles of, 266–267

   base of, 266

   congruent, determining,
      264–267

   defined, 266, 277

   diagonals of, 267

   properties of, determining,
      264, 266

Index

Isosceles triangle

Defined, 204

in coordinate plane, classifying, 498–499

points of concurrency of, 503

K

Kites

defined, 259, 277

delta conyne, 266

diagonals of, 263, 265, 277

diamond, 263–265

properties of, determining, 264

Knot, 242

L

Linear functions

average rate of change, calculating in, 89–91

defined, 18

interpreting graphs of, 21–22

problem situations, modeling with, 15–22

representing

using equations, 17–18, 20

using graphs, 17, 18

using tables, 16

using words, 15–16

Line of reflection, 382, 384

Lines

distance between lines and points, 489–492

slopes of, 480, 481

Line symmetry, 21, 85–88

Logic, 99–134

Logically equivalent, 122

Logical reasoning

methods of, 101–106

used in conditional statements, 111, 122

M

Mathematical sequence, 57

Mean, 344, 346, 348

Measure of central tendency

defined, 344

mean, 221, 344, 346, 348

median, 345, 346, 348

mode, 345, 348

for samples, calculating, 348, 350

Median, 221, 345, 346, 348

Midpoint, 473–477, 497

Midpoint Formula, 477

Midsegments, 497

Mixture problems, solving, 438–441

Mode, 345, 348

Monomial, 151

Multiplication

repeated, exponents used to indicate, 45

simplifying before, 176

Multiplication table, 161–162

N

Negation

of the conclusion, 227

of conditional statement, 123

Negative reciprocal, 484–485

Negative sign, distributing, 151

Number laws. See Real number laws

O

Obtuse triangle, 196

Odd functions, 393–394

Open points, 35

Opposite angles, 270

Opposite sides, 269

Orthocenters, 223, 503

Outcomes of probability, 294–295, 297–300

See also Sample space

Outlier, 360

P

Paragraph proof, 240, 267

Parallel lines

determining, 481

equations of, determining, 481–482

Parallelograms

congruent angles of, 270, 271

congruent sides of, 270, 271, 272

consecutive angles of, 269

consecutive sides of, 269

defined, 259, 260, 261, 277

diagonals of, 271, 272, 276–277

opposite angles of, 270

opposite sides of, 269, 270

properties of, 272, 276

as quadrilateral, verifying, 511–513

supplementary angles of, 270, 271

Pentagon

external angles of, measures of, 287, 288, 290

identifying, 117, 119, 121, 279

interior angles of, measures of, 280, 283, 285, 287–288, 290

regular, 283, 287–288

vertex of, finding, 290

Perfect squares, 173–174

Permutations

calculating with/without repeated elements, 316–317

circular, calculating, 318–319

defined, 316

notations used for, 316

probabilities calculated by
using, 321

sample space size calculated
by using, 313–314

strings as examples of,
313–314, 316

Permutations key, 316

Perpendicular bisector, 216–217,
219, 222

Perpendicular lines

determining, 482–483

equations of, determining,
485

slopes of, 484

Point of intersection, 396–398

Points

determining distance between
two, 465–469

distance between lines and
points, 489–492

perpendicular distance from,
to a line, 215

representing endpoints in
graphs, 35

Points of concurrency

centroid, 499–500

constructing, 501

defined, 215

of isosceles triangle, 503

solving for, algebraically, 500

in triangle, 224

Point-slope form, 481

Polygon

convex, 281, 287, 290

diagonal connecting single
vertex of, 280, 282

exterior angles of

defined, 287

measure of, determining,
288, 289–290

sum of, determining, 288,
289–290

interior angles of

convex polygon,
determining sum of, 280,
289, 290

defined, 280

regular polygon, determining
measure of, 287–288, 289

regular, 283, 290

sides of, determining number
of, 282–283

See also Hexagon; Pentagon

Polynomial equations

defined, 417

solving, 417–418

Polynomials

adding or subtracting, using
area models,
151–154

binomial, 151

defined, 151

dividing

using area models, 159–160

using long division, 162–163

using multiplication table,
161–162

factoring, using square roots,
173

functions, transforming using
graphs,
415–416

greatest common factor of,
418–420

monomial, 151

multiplying, using area
models, 154–156,
157–159

operations with, 151–156

trinomials

defined, 151

factoring, using area
models, 164–165

quadratic, 159, 167–171

Population data

analyzing by collecting and
comparing samples,
347–358

measure of central tendency
in, 344–346

trimodal, 345

See also Samples

Postulate, 126

Predictions

using graphs to make, 6, 8,
13, 42–44

using sample data to make,
365–368

Probability

calculating, using
combinations and
permutations, 313–321

compound, 301–309

of compound events, 295

conditional, 310–311

defined, 293–294

of dependent events, 296

of desired outcomes, 294

of expected value, 329–332

experimental *vs.* theoretical,
333–337

independent trials and,
323–328

outcomes, 294–295, 297–300

ratio, determining, 206–209

sample spaces and, 293–300

with/without replacement, 296,
304

See also Independent events
of probability

Proof by contradiction

defined, 132

negation of the conclusion
and, 227

proving statements with,
132

proving Triangle Exterior Angle
Theorem, 227, 230–231

Proof by contrapositive, 109

Propositional form, 113

Propositional variables, 113

Pythagorean Theorem, 174–175

Q

Quadratic equations

roots of, 407–411

solving, 408–411

Index

Index

equilateral, 204, 504

Exterior Angle Inequality Theorem and, proving, 202, 228–229

exterior angles of, 198–200, 287

hypotenuse of right triangle and vertices of the triangle, 496–497

incenter, 214–215, 224, 503

inequality property, 228

interior angle measures, sum of, 280

inscribed in circles, 494–496

isosceles, 204

median, 221

midsegments of, 488–489

negation of the conclusion, 227

obtuse, 196

orthocenters, 223

paragraph proof, using to show congruency, 240

perpendicular bisector, 216–217, 219, 222

points of concurrency, 211–224

probability ratio of, determining, 206–209

properties of, 193–253

proving theorems, 228–229, 232

relationship between measures, determining, 199–200, 205–207

using a graphing calculator, 208–209

relationship between measures, using to solve problems, 200–201

remote interior angles of, identifying, 199

right, 196

scalene, 203, 505–506

segment bisector, 217–218

side relationships of, 203–209

sides shared with, identifying, 236

slope of, determining, 495

Triangle Exterior Angle Theorem and, proving, 225–227, 230–231

Triangle Sum Theorem and, 195, 199, 203

two-column proof, 225–226

vertices shared by, identifying, 235

wind, 241–244

See also Congruent triangles, proving

Triangle strip, 235

Triangle Sum Theorem, 195, 199, 203

Trimodal data set, 345

Trinomials

defined, 151

factoring, using area models, 164–165

quadratic, 159, 167–171

Truth table, 115

Truth value, 113–116

Two-column proof, 225–226

V

Venn diagram, 261

Vertical motion, 27

Vertical translation of a graph, 371–373

Vertical lines

defined, 487

determining, 487–488

slope of, undefined, 487

W

Wind triangle, 241–244

With/without replacement

compound probability, 304

defined, 296

probability of independent events, 296

Work problems, solving, 435–437

Y

Y-intercepts, 86–88, 481

X

X-intercepts, 86–88, 413

Z

Zeros

of functions vs. roots of equations, 455–457

of quadratic functions, calculating, 412–414

x-intercepts of a function and, 413